My Fun with Learning

1

Great Stories
from
World Literature

The Southwestern Company

Nashville, Tennessee

ACKNOWLEDGMENTS:

TEXT

"In Which Pooh Goes Visiting and Gets Into a Tight Place," from *Winnie-the-Pooh* by A. A. Milne. Copyright 1926 by E. P. Dutton, renewed 1954 by A. A. Milne. Reprinted by permission of the publisher, E. P. Dutton, a division of NAL Penguin, Inc.

Stone Soup by Marcia Brown. Copyright 1947 Marcia Brown; copyright renewed © 1975 Marcia Brown. Reprinted with permission of Charles Scribner's Sons, a division of Macmillan, Inc.

The Crane Wife retold by Sumiko Yagawa. Translated by Katherine Paterson. Copyright 1979 by Sumiko Yagawa. Reprinted by permission of Morrow Jr. (a division of William Morrow & Company, Inc.).

"Puss in Boots" and "Cinderella" by Eleanor Graham Vance from *The Tall Book of Fairy Tales* © 1947 by Western Publishing Company, Inc. Used by permission.

"The Ugly Duckling" by Hans Christian Andersen. Translated by Erik Christian Haugaard from *The Complete Fairy Tales and Stories of Hans Christian Andersen*. Copyright © 1974 by Erik Christian Haugaard. Reprinted by permission of Doubleday Publishing Group.

"The King's Drum" from *The King's Drum and Other African Stories* by Harold Courlander. Copyright 1962 by Harold Courlander. Published by Harcourt Brace and World, Inc.

"Paul's Great Flapjack Griddle" by Wallace Wadsworth from *Paul Bunyan and His Great Blue Ox*. Copyright 1926 by George H. Doran Company. Reprinted by permission of Doubleday & Company.

"Balloons *and* Balloons" from *Mary Poppins Comes Back*. Copyright 1935, 1963 by P. L. Travers. Reprinted by permission of Harcourt Brace Jovanovich, Inc.

ILLUSTRATIONS

Joseph Forte pp. 114–128, 142–147, 153–163
Kim Mulkey pp. 13, 48–51, 58–63, 98–108, 112, 152, 164–171, 186
Jo Polseno pp. 6–12, 14–40, 68–79, 140
Yuri Salzman pp. 42–47, 64–67, 80–96, 130–138, 204–222
Patricia J. Wynne pp. 52–56, 110–111, 148–151, 174–185, 187–201, 224

Produced by The Hudson Group, Inc.
Designed by Carlo De Lucia

Copyright 1994, 1993, 1992, 1991, 1990, 1989, 1988 by The Southwestern Company
Printed in the United States of America

A Note for Parents

The stories and poems collected in this volume offer beginning readers an exciting and enriching introduction to world literature. Here are some of the world's best fables, fairy tales, stories, and poems written for young people.

This book begins with easy-to-read fables and stories. As beginning readers go further into the book, their reading skills will improve as they encounter more difficult selections.

This book gives young readers the opportunity to learn about the different kinds of literature that they should know and love. They will learn to continue their reading by searching for other books of the same kind and by the same famous authors. These books are readily available in libraries and bookstores.

Great Stories from World Literature is invaluable for children who have not yet learned to read. While parents or older children read aloud to them, they can recognize new words and begin to read for themselves. They will enjoy the beautiful illustrations. When they have learned to read by themselves, the children will enjoy the stories and poems all the more. This book helps make the transition from listener to reader easy and fun.

Among the selections are some of the most popular fables of Aesop, stories based on Greek mythology, classic fairy tales, and stories with settings as far away as England, Europe, India, Africa, and Japan. Included are tales by such masters as Hans Christian Andersen, A. A. Milne, Lewis Carroll, and Rudyard Kipling.

American literature is also well represented, with selections from Nathaniel Hawthorne, Henry Wadsworth Longfellow, Mark Twain, and others. Young readers will enjoy the adventures of American literary characters such as Tom Sawyer, Paul Bunyan, and the mighty Casey of baseball fame.

This volume will help young readers prepare for the great adventure of learning that awaits them. The following volumes in MY FUN WITH LEARNING cover subjects that all young people should know, including science, geography, the adventure of space, and history.

Contents

Great Stories From World Literature

Sally and Sam were sitting in Sam's house, looking out the window. The rain was falling steadily, and it was too rainy to play outside.

"I know," Sam said. "Let's read some of Aesop's fables. Aesop lived long ago in Greece. Each of his stories has something interesting to say. And the characters in the stories—lots of times they are animals, sometimes they are people, and sometimes natural things like the sun and the wind."

"He must have had some imagination!" Sally said.

"He sure did," Sam replied. "Look, this one is about a goose that laid a golden egg."

6

The Goose That Laid a Golden Egg

AESOP

"DEAR WIFE," said the farmer as he sat down to his breakfast, "I wish we didn't have to work so hard."

"I don't mind," said his wife. "We have enough to eat, clothes to wear, and a warm house."

"That's not enough for me," the farmer said. "I want to be rich."

After breakfast, the farmer's wife went out to the house where they kept their geese. There among the eggs the geese had laid was a yellow egg. She knew that something strange had happened and so she told her husband about it.

"Why this egg is made of gold," he said. "Show me which goose laid the egg."

They went out to look at the geese but they could not tell which goose had laid the golden egg.

"I know what to do," said the farmer. "I will kill the geese one by one until I find the one that has golden eggs inside."

"Why not be content to wait until it lays another golden egg? One golden egg will buy so much for us until we find the next one."

But the farmer couldn't fight his greed. He killed his geese one by one and found no more golden eggs. What's more, all his fine geese never again would lay eggs at all.

GREED CAN KILL THE GOOSE THAT LAYS A GOLDEN EGG.

7

This story illustrates what can happen when we try too hard to do what other people think we should, rather than what we think is the right thing. Like all of Aesop's fables, this tale is very simple, but the lesson it teaches is a valuable one.

The Man, the Boy, and the Donkey

AESOP

A MAN AND HIS SON were going with their donkey to market. As they were walking along, a countryman passed them and said, "You fools, what is a donkey for but to ride upon?"

So the man put the boy on the donkey and they went on their way. Soon they passed a group of men. One of them said, "See that lazy youngster? He lets his father walk while he rides."

So the man ordered his boy to get off, and got on himself. They hadn't gone far when they passed two women. One woman said to the other, "Shame on that lazy lout, to let his poor little son trudge along beside that big, strong donkey!"

Well, the man didn't know what to do. At last he took his boy up before him on the donkey. By this time they had come to the town. The passersby began to jeer and point at them. The man stopped and asked what they were scoffing at. The men said, "Aren't you ashamed of yourself for overloading that poor donkey of yours—you and your hulking son?"

The man and the boy got off and tried to think what to do. They thought and they thought. At last they cut down a pole, tied the donkey's feet to it, and raised the pole and the donkey to their shoulders. They went along amid the laughter of all who met them till they came

8

to Market Bridge. The donkey, getting one of his feet loose, kicked out and caused the boy to drop his end of the pole. In the struggle the donkey fell over the bridge. His forefeet being tied together, he was drowned.

"That will teach you," said an old man who had followed them.

PLEASE ALL, AND YOU WILL PLEASE NONE.

In this fable the main characters are not people or even animals, but natural forces—the sun and the wind. They have human qualities and abilities, just as animals do in other fables of Aesop. They can talk with one another, disagree with one another, and even have a little friendly competition.

The Sun and the Wind

AESOP

THE WIND DECIDED one day that he was the strongest creature in the sky. As soon as the Sun came out that day, he said, "My friend the Sun, let's have a contest to see who is stronger?"

This idea did not seem very good to the kindly Sun, who had only just come out. "If you please, Wind, I would just as soon not do that. I have a long day ahead of me to spread my sunshine."

"I believe you know I am stronger than you. If you will just say that, I will find someone else to play this game with me."

At this the Sun became a bit annoyed with the Wind and decided after all that he would be willing to try his strength.

"How shall we play our game?" said the Sun.

"I know," said the Wind. "There's a traveler down below who is wearing a heavy coat. Let's see who can get that coat off the traveler's back. I'll go first."

The Wind blew and blew as hard as he could. But whenever the Wind blew, the traveler wrapped his coat tighter and tighter about him. Finally, the Wind could blow no more.

Then the Sun turned on his kindly rays and warmed the traveler up until the man had no need for his coat. Soon enough, the man took off his coat and carried it on his arm.

"You win," said the Wind, who had learned a lesson.

KINDLY ACTIONS CAN DO MORE THAN FORCE.

How many times have you looked at a problem and tried again and again to find a solution, only to be disappointed each time? And then, just as you are ready to give up, a new idea occurs to you, and it works. Then you say to yourself, "Why didn't I think of that first?" This fable concerns a crow with a real problem, and his life depends on finding the solution.

The Crow and the Pitcher

AESOP

A CROW, almost dead with thirst, came upon a pitcher that once had been filled with water. But when the crow put his beak into the pitcher to drink, he found there was only a little water at the bottom. The crow tried and tried but could not reach the water. Then he tried to overturn the pitcher, but it would not budge. Finally, the crow tried to break the pitcher, but it was too well made.

The crow was about to give up his effort when a new idea came to him. He picked up a pebble and dropped it into the pitcher. Then he picked up another pebble and dropped it into the pitcher. He continued to drop pebbles into the pitcher, and slowly the water rose toward the top. Then the crow was able to drink the water and save himself.

NECESSITY IS THE MOTHER OF INVENTION.

We all know people who keep putting off things they should do. So we can all imagine ourselves in the position of the grasshopper in this fable. After you read the story, ask yourself this question: Would you have behaved the way the grasshopper did?

The Ant and the Grasshopper,

AESOP

ALL DAY LONG all through the warm days of summer, a green grasshopper went happily about. Whenever the grasshopper was thirsty, he would sip nectar from any plant he saw.

One afternoon, as the grasshopper was leaping from flower to flower, he saw beneath him a little black ant struggling to carry a fat leaf bigger than himself.

"Little friend," said the grasshopper, "what are you doing down there?"

"Why, I am carrying this leaf off to my nest. I must fill my nest with food to last through winter."

"Winter?" said the grasshopper. "Who cares about winter? Why don't you climb up to this flower and enjoy its sweet nectar? Winter will take care of itself."

"That isn't the way things work in this world," said the ant. "Winter will be here soon. The flowers will be gone, and there will be nothing to eat."

"Well, suit yourself," said the grasshopper. And off he went, singing happily and having no cares at all.

The ant returned to his work. It took all his strength to carry each leaf, but he did not mind. He knew he would have enough to last the winter.

Soon the cold weather came. The ant was snug in his nest with plenty of food to eat. The grasshopper? He had nothing to eat and soon was no more.

A WISE PERSON KNOWS THAT SUMMER DOES NOT LAST FOREVER.

It was just after lunchtime on Saturday afternoon. Sam and Sally had spent the morning riding their bicycles. Now they were sitting under a tree in Sam's front yard, trying to think of something interesting to do.

"I know," said Sally, and she ran across the yard and into her house. In a minute she returned with a book.

"Let's read some stories," she suggested to Sam, who was lying on his back looking up at the sky. "Look, these are the fairy tales my Mom and Dad read to me when I was too young to read. Dad said the stories are hundreds of years old. They were told to kids by their parents for a long time before they were ever written down."

"Good thing somebody did write them down," Sam said. "Read them to me, Sally, while I lie here and watch the clouds change their shapes."

Little Red Riding Hood

Adapted from The Blue Fairy Book,
Collected by Andrew Lang

ONCE UPON A TIME there lived in a small village the prettiest little country girl that was ever seen. Her Mother loved her very much. And so did her Grandmother. This good woman made the little girl a little red riding hood, which was so becoming that everybody called the little girl Little Red Riding Hood.

One day her Mother, having made some pies, said to her, "Go, my dear, and take this pie to your Grandmother, and take this jar of jam too. See how she is, for I have heard she has a cold and is not feeling well."

And so Little Red Riding Hood set out immediately to go to her Grandmother, who lived in another village.

As Little Red Riding Hood was going through the wood she met a Wolf. The Wolf wanted to eat her up, but decided not to because he could hear woodsmen working nearby. Instead, he asked Little Red Riding Hood where she was going.

The girl, who did not know it was dangerous to talk with a Wolf in the forest, said, "I am going to visit my Grandmother and take her a pie and some jam my Mother made."

"Does she live far away?" asked the Wolf.

"Oh, yes," answered Little Red Riding Hood. "Her house is beyond that mill you see there, at the first house in the village."

"Well," said the Wolf, "I'll go and visit her too. I'll go this way and you go that, and we shall see who gets there first."

The Wolf began to trot as fast as he could, taking the shortest way. Little Red Riding Hood took the path, which was a longer way to go, and stopped to collect nuts, chase butterflies, and gather flowers. And so the Wolf got to Grandmother's house well ahead of Little Red Riding Hood.

The Wolf knocked at the door—tap, tap, tap.

"Who's there?" Grandmother said.

"Your grandchild, Little Red Riding Hood," the Wolf replied, changing his voice so he would sound like the young girl. "I have brought you a pie and some jam from my Mother."

Grandmother, who was sick in bed, said, "Pull the bobbin, and the door latch will go up."

The Wolf pulled on the bobbin, and the door opened. In an instant the Wolf was on the poor Grandmother and ate her all up.

A short time later, Little Red Riding Hood got to Grandmother's house. She knocked at the door—tap, tap, tap.

"Who's there?" called the Wolf.

Upon hearing the Wolf's big, deep voice, Little Red

Riding Hood was afraid at first. Then she remembered that Grandmother had a bad cold and might be hoarse. She answered, "It is your grandchild, Little Red Riding Hood. I have brought you a pie and some jam from my Mother."

The Wolf, trying this time to disguise his voice, said, "Pull the bobbin, and the door latch will go up."

Little Red Riding Hood pulled the bobbin, and the door opened.

The Wolf had put on one of Grandmother's night-gowns and was in bed with the sheets and blanket pulled right up to his chin.

"Put the pie and jam there on the table," said the Wolf, "and come sit here on the bed beside your dear old Grandma."

When Little Red Riding Hood sat on the bed, she was amazed at how her Grandma looked.

"Oh, Grandmother," she said, "what great arms you have."

"All the better to hug you with, my dear," the Wolf quickly replied.

"Oh, Grandmother, what great ears you have."

"All the better to hear you with, my dear."

"Oh, Grandmother, what great eyes you have."

"All the better to see you with, my child."

"Oh, Grandmother, what great *teeth* you have."

"All the better to *eat* you with," cried the Wolf, who jumped out of bed and began chasing Little Red Riding Hood all around the room.

A woodsman passing nearby heard the commotion and came to investigate. He took one look at the Wolf and knocked him on the head. After the Wolf was dead the woodsman could still hear a voice coming from the Wolf's body, so he took out his knife and cut open the Wolf. There was Grandmother. She was so happy to be freed that she forgot all about her cold, and all three of them—the woodsman, Grandmother, and Little Red Riding Hood—had pie and jam together!

This is one of the all-time favorite stories for children. Some versions of the story replace Goldilocks with a character described as a "Little Old Woman." There is also a fairy tale about a girl named Goldilocks that has nothing to do with three bears. But the tale below is the one most familiar to readers young and old.

Goldilocks and the Three Bears

Adapted from The Green Fairy Book, *Collected by Andrew Lang*

ONCE UPON A TIME there were three bears who lived together in a house of their own in a wood. One of them was a great, huge Papa Bear. One was a middle-sized Mama Bear. And one was a little, small, tiny, wee Baby Bear.

They each had a bowl for their porridge. A great bowl for the great, huge Papa Bear. A middle-sized bowl for the Mama Bear. And a little bowl for the little, small, tiny, wee Baby Bear.

They each had a chair to sit in. A great chair for the great, huge Papa Bear. A middle-sized chair for the Mama Bear. And a little chair for the little, small, tiny, wee Baby Bear.

One day after they had made the porridge for their breakfast and poured it into their bowls, they went for a walk to let the porridge cool so it would not burn their mouths.

While they were walking, along came a pretty little girl named Goldilocks. She was well named, for her hair was the color of gold and tumbled down to her shoulders in beautiful curls. When she came to the house of the three bears, she was curious to see who might live there. First she looked in at the window, and then

she peeped in at the keyhole. Seeing nobody in the house, she tried the door latch.

The door opened. It was not locked because the bears were good bears. They did nobody any harm and never thought anybody would harm them.

Goldilocks went into the house. There she saw the three bowls of porridge on the table. If the bears had been home, they would have invited her to breakfast. But little Goldilocks was not a well-mannered little girl, and she did not wait. She decided to help herself.

She tasted the porridge in the bowl of the great, huge Papa Bear. It was too hot. Then she tasted the porridge in the middle-sized bowl of the Mama Bear. It was too cold. Then she tasted the porridge in the bowl of the little, small, tiny, wee Baby Bear. It was just right. So she ate it all up.

Then Goldilocks saw the three chairs in the room, and decided to sit for a while. First she sat in the great chair of the great, huge Papa Bear, but it was too hard. Then she tried the middle-sized chair of the Mama Bear, but it was too soft. Then she tried the little chair of the little, small, tiny, wee Baby Bear. It was neither too hard nor too soft. It was just right. But just as she was getting comfortable in it, the little chair broke. Down she fell, thump, right on the floor.

Then Goldilocks wandered upstairs to the bedroom where the three bears slept. There she found the great bed of the great, huge Pape Bear, and the middle-sized bed of the Mama Bear, and the little bed of the little, small, tiny, wee Baby Bear.

Suddenly Goldilocks became very sleepy, so she lay down in the Papa Bear's great bed, but it was too high at the head for her. Then she tried the middle-sized bed of the Mama Bear, but it was too high at the foot for her. Then she tried the little bed of the little, small, tiny, wee Baby Bear. It was neither too high at the head nor too high at the foot. It was just right. So she covered herself up comfortably and fell fast asleep.

By this time the three bears thought their porridge would be cool enough, so they came home to have breakfast.

Goldilocks had left the spoon of the Papa Bear standing in his porridge. "Somebody has been at my porridge!" said the great, huge Papa Bear, in his great, gruff voice.

When the Mama Bear looked at hers, she saw the spoon was standing in it too. "Somebody has been at *my* porridge!" she said, in her middle-sized voice.

Then the little, small, tiny, wee Baby Bear looked at his, and the spoon was in the bowl, but the porridge was all gone.

"Somebody has been at *my* porridge," he said in his little, small, tiny, wee voice, "and has eaten it up!"

Then the three bears began to look about them. Now, Goldilocks had not put the cushion back properly on the Papa Bear's great chair after she had tried it.

"Somebody has been sitting in my chair," said the great, huge Papa Bear, in his great, gruff voice.

And Goldilocks had twisted the soft cushion on the Mama Bear's middle-sized chair.

"Somebody has been sitting in *my* chair," said the Mama Bear, in her middle-sized voice.

And the little, small, tiny, wee Baby Bear looked at his chair.

"Somebody has been sitting in *my* chair, and its all broken," he said, in his small, tiny, little, wee voice.

Then the three bears went upstairs to their bedchamber. The Papa Bear looked at his great, huge bed and saw that the pillow was out of place.

"Somebody has been sleeping in my bed," said the Papa Bear, in his great, gruff voice.

The Mama Bear saw that the blanket of her middle-sized bed had been wrinkled up.

"Somebody has been sleeping in *my* bed," she said, in her middle-sized voice.

And when the Baby Bear came to look at his little, small, tiny, wee bed, he was the most surprised of all.

"Somebody has been sleeping in *my* bed," he said in his little, small, tiny, wee voice, "and here she is!"

Goldilocks in her sleep had heard the great, gruff voice of the Papa Bear, but it had seemed to her like the roaring wind or the rumbling thunder. And she had heard the middle-sized voice of the Mama Bear, but it was only as if she had heard someone speaking in a dream. But the little, small, tiny, wee voice of the Baby Bear was so close that she woke up at once.

Goldilocks sat up in the bed with a start. She looked and there, standing at the side of the bed, were the three bears staring at her.

Goldilocks tumbled out the other side of the bed and, seeing the bedchamber window open, out she jumped. No sooner did her feet light on the ground than they carried the little girl away from the house and along the path through the woods. And the three bears never saw her again.

It is no surprise that Walt Disney chose this story for one of his best animated films. It is a story of conflict, of the struggle between good and evil. Add one magic mirror, one wicked queen, one beautiful young princess, and seven dwarfs, and you have a very special fairy tale.

Snow White and the Seven Dwarfs

Adapted from the Tale Snow-Drop, *Collected by Jacob and Wilhelm Grimm*

IN THE MIDDLE OF WINTER, when the broad flakes of snow were falling all around, a Queen sat working at a window whose frame was made of fine black ebony. And as she looked out upon the snow, she pricked her finger. Three drops of blood fell upon the snow. Then she gazed thoughtfully at the red drops that sprinkled the white snow, and said, "Would that my little daughter may be as white as that snow, as red as the blood, and as black as the ebony window frame!"

And the Queen got her wish. The little girl grew, and her skin was as white as snow, her cheeks as rosy as the blood, and her hair as black as ebony. And she was called Snow White.

But the Queen died, and the King soon took another wife, who was very beautiful, but so proud that she could not bear the idea that anyone might be more beautiful. She had a magic mirror, to which she used to go every day. She would look at herself in the mirror and say,

> Mirror, mirror, on the wall,
> Who is the fairest one of all?

And the mirror would answer,

> You, Queen, are the fairest one of all.

But Snow White grew more and more beautiful, and by the time she was seven years old, she was as bright as the day, and fairer even than the Queen herself. Then one day, when the Queen asked her mirror the question, the answer was:

Queen, thou may fair and beauteous be,
But Snow White is more fair than thee.

When the Queen heard this, she turned pale with rage and envy. She called to one of her servants and said, "Take Snow White away into the wide wood, and make sure I never see her again."

The servant led Snow White away to the forest. But his heart melted when she begged him to spare her life, and he said, "I cannot hurt you, pretty one." So he decided not to kill her, but to leave her to her fate in the forest. He thought she would probably be killed by the wild animals.

Snow White wandered along through the wood in great fear. The wild animals roared about her, but none did her any harm. In the evening she came to a little cottage, and went inside to find a place to rest, for she could walk no more.

Everything in the cottage was neat and tidy. On the table was spread a white cloth, and there were seven little plates with seven little loaves of bread, and seven little glasses with wine in them. Seven knives and seven forks were laid in their proper places. And by the wall stood seven little beds.

Snow White was very hungry. She took a little piece from each loaf of bread, and drank a sip of wine out of each glass. After that she decided to lie down and rest. So she tried each of the little beds. The first was too long, the next was too short, and so on, till at last she found the seventh bed to her liking, and there she lay herself down and fell asleep.

After a time, in came the masters of the cottage. They were seven little dwarfs, who worked in the mountains and dug and searched about for gold and

silver. They lighted their seven lamps, and saw quickly that all was not right.

The first said, "Who has been sitting on my stool?"

The second said, "Who has been eating off my plate?"

The third said, "Who has been picking at my bread?"

The fourth said, "Who has been meddling with my spoon?"

The fifth said, "Who has been handling my fork?"

The sixth said, "Who has been cutting with my knife?"

The seventh said, "Who has been drinking my wine?"

Then the first looked round and said, "Who has been lying in my bed?" And the rest looked round at their beds, and every one cried out that somebody had been upon his bed. But the seventh saw Snow White and cried out to his fellows to come look. They all stood in 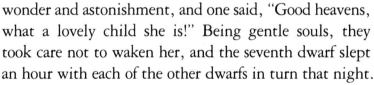 wonder and astonishment, and one said, "Good heavens, what a lovely child she is!" Being gentle souls, they took care not to waken her, and the seventh dwarf slept an hour with each of the other dwarfs in turn that night.

In the morning, Snow White told them her story. The dwarfs took pity on her and said if she would keep their house in order for them, she could stay and they would take care of her. This pleased the girl very much, and she agreed.

Then the dwarfs went out to their day's work, seeking gold and silver in the mountains. But before they left, they warned Snow White, saying, "The Queen will soon find out where you are, so take care and let no one in."

The Queen, thinking now that Snow White was dead, believed herself to be the handsomest lady in the land. So she went to her mirror and said,

Mirror, mirror on the wall,
Who is the fairest of them all?

And the mirror answered,

You, Queen, are fairest in all this land,
But over the hills in the greenwood shade,
Where the dwarfs their dwelling have made,

There Snow White is hiding her head, and
Is lovelier, far, O Queen, than thee.

The Queen became furious when she heard this. She knew the mirror never lied, and realized that her servant had disobeyed her.

She could not bear to think that anyone was more beautiful than she. So she disguised herself as an old peddler and went to the cottage where the dwarfs lived. When she got there, she knocked at the door and cried, "Fine wares to sell!"

Snow White looked out at the window, and said, "Good day, good woman. What have you to sell?"

"Good wares, fine wares," said she. "Laces and bobbins of all colors."

"I will let the old lady in," thought Snow White. "She seems to be a very good sort of person." So she ran down and unbolted the door.

"Oh, my," said the old woman, "how badly your dress is laced! Here, take one of my nice new laces." Snow White did not dream she was in any danger, but soon the old woman pulled the lace so tight that Snow White couldn't breathe and in a moment she fell down in a dead faint.

"There's an end of your beauty," said the spiteful Queen, and she went home.

In the evening the seven dwarfs returned to find Snow White stretched upon the floor, pale and motionless, as if she were dead. They lifted her up and, finding what was the matter, cut the lace. In a while Snow White began to breathe, and the color came back into her cheeks.

After Snow White told them what had happened, the dwarfs said, "That old woman was the Queen herself. Take care in the future. And let no one in when we are away."

When the Queen got home, she went straight to the mirror, and asked the usual question. To her great surprise, once more it said,

You, Queen, are the fairest in all this
    land,
But over the hills in the greenwood
    shade,
Where the dwarfs their dwelling have
    made,
There Snow White is hiding her head,
    and
Is lovelier, far, O Queen, than thee.

The blood ran cold in her heart at the thought that
Snow White still lived. The Queen dressed herself up
again in a disguise, but very different from the one she
wore before, and took with her a poisoned comb.

When she reached the dwarfs' cottage, she knocked
at the door, and cried, "Fine wares to sell."

But Snow White said, "I dare not let anyone in."

Then the Queen said, "Just look at my beautiful
combs," and held up the poisoned one. The comb was
so lovely that Snow White put it to her hair to try it.
But the poison on it was so powerful that the moment
the comb touched her lovely young head, Snow White
fell down senseless.

"Lie there, my lovely," said the Queen, and went
her way.

Fortunately, the dwarfs returned very early that evening, and when they saw Snow White lying on the
ground, they ran to her and soon found the poisoned
comb. After they removed it, Snow White recovered
and told them what had happened. Again the dwarfs
warned her not to let anyone in when they were away.

Meantime the Queen went home to her mirror, and
trembled with rage when she received exactly the same
answer as before. She said, "Snow White shall die, if
it costs me my life."

The Queen went into her secret chamber and there
prepared a poisoned apple. The apple looked juicy and
tasty, but whoever should eat it would surely die.

Then she dressed herself up as a peasant's wife and

traveled over the hills to the dwarfs' cottage. She knocked at the door, but Snow White put her head out of the window and said, "I dare not let anyone in."

"Do as you please," said the old woman, "but take this lovely, delicious apple. I will make you a present of it."

"No," said Snow White, "I dare not take it."

"Silly girl," answered the old woman, "what are you afraid of? Do you think it is poisoned? Come, you eat one part of it, and I will eat the other."

Now the apple was prepared so that one side was good, though the other side was poisoned. The old woman took her bite from the good side, then gave the apple to Snow White, who bit into the poisoned side and instantly fell down, lifeless.

"This time nothing can save you," said the Queen.

And when she returned to her mirror, at last it said,

You, Queen, are the fairest one of all.

Then her spiteful heart was glad, if such a heart as hers can ever be.

That evening when the dwarfs returned home they found Snow White lying motionless before the window. No breath passed her lips, and she appeared to be quite dead. They lifted her up and combed her hair and washed her face with wine and water, but she did not awaken. So they laid her down, and all seven watched and mourned three whole days.

Then they discussed what was to be done with Snow White. Her cheeks were still rosy, and her face looked just as it did while she was alive, so they decided not to bury her. Instead, they made a glass coffin, that they might still look at her, and upon it they wrote her name in gold letters, and that she was a king's daughter. And the coffin was placed upon the hill, and one of the dwarfs always sat by it and watched. And even the birds came and mourned the death of Snow White.

And thus Snow White lay for a long, long time, and still she looked as though she were asleep. Then one day a prince passed by the dwarfs' cottage and saw Snow White. He read what was written on the coffin. Then he begged the dwarfs to let him take her away, but they could not bear to give her up.

Still the prince beseeched them, and finally they agreed to let him take Snow White. But the moment he lifted up the coffin to carry it away, the piece of apple fell from between her lips, and Snow White awoke and said, "Where am I?"

And the prince answered, "You are safe with me." Then he told her all that had happened, and said, "I love you better than all the world. Come with me to my father's palace, and you shall be my wife." And Snow White consented and went home with the prince.

Everything was prepared with great pomp and splendor for their wedding. Among those invited to the fine

wedding feast was the wicked Queen, and as she was
dressing herself in her fine, rich clothes, she looked in
her mirror and asked,

Mirror, mirror on the wall,

Who is the fairest one of all?

And the mirror answered,

Queen, thou may fair and beauteous be,

But the new Queen is more fair than thee.

When she heard this she was filled with hatred. But
her envy and curiosity were so great that she decided
to go see this bride. And when she arrived and saw that
it was none other than Snow White, she choked with
her own anger and hatred and died on the spot.

And Snow White and the prince lived and reigned
happily over that land for many, many years.

Sometimes characters in fairy tales do things that we in the real world know we should not do. For example, we know it is wrong to steal anything from anyone. This story is about a boy who takes several things—from an ogre who eats little boys for breakfast! Do you think young Jack is right in doing what he does?

Jack and the Beanstalk

Adapted from English Fairy Tales,
Collected by Joseph Jacobs

ONCE UPON A TIME there was a poor widow who had an only son named Jack and a cow named Milky White. All they had to live on was the milk the cow gave every morning, which they took to the market and sold. But one morning Milky White gave no milk, and they didn't know what to do.

"What shall we do, what shall we do?" said the widow, wringing her hands.

"Cheer up, Mother, I'll go and get some kind of work somewhere," said Jack.

"We've tried that before, and nobody would take you," said his Mother. "We must sell Milky White and with the money open a shop, or something."

"All right, Mother," said Jack. "It's market day today, and I'll soon sell Milky White. Then we'll see what we can do."

So he took the cow's halter in his hand, and off he started. He hadn't gone far when he met a funny looking old man, who said to him, "Good morning."

"Good morning to you," said Jack.

"Where are you going?" the man asked.

"I'm going to market to sell our cow."

"Oh, I bet you'll strike a good bargain for your cow," said the man. "Say, do you know how many beans it takes to make five?"

"Two in each hand and one in your mouth," said Jack, as sharp as a tack.

"Right you are," said the man, "and here they are, the very beans themselves," he went on, pulling out of his pocket a number of strange beans. "As you are so clever," said he, "I don't mind doing a swap with you— your cow for these beans."

"Ho ho," laughed Jack, "that would be a nice trade— but only for you."

"Ah! You don't know what these beans are," said the man. "If you plant them overnight, by morning they grow right up to the sky."

"Really?" said Jack. "You don't say."

"Yes, it's true, and if it doesn't turn out just so, you can have your cow back."

"All right," said Jack, and he handed over Milky White's halter and pocketed the beans.

"Back already, Jack?" said his Mother when he got home. "I see you haven't got Milky White, so you've sold her. How much did you get for her?"

"You'll never guess, Mother," said Jack.

"Really? Good boy! Five pounds! Ten! Fifteen? No, it can't be twenty?"

"I told you you couldn't guess. What do you say to these beans! They're magical. Plant them overnight and . . . ."

"What!" exclaimed Jack's Mother. "Have you been such a fool as to give away Milky White, the best milker in the county, for five little beans?" Then she threw the beans out the window and sent Jack off to bed without his supper.

Jack went upstairs to his little room in the attic, as sorry to have disappointed his Mother as he was sad at not getting supper.

At last he dropped off to sleep.

When he woke up, the room looked odd. The sun was shining into part of it, and yet the rest of it was quite dark. Jack jumped up and dressed himself and went to the window. And there he saw, rising from the spot where his Mother had tossed the beans the day before, the biggest beanstalk he had ever seen. It went up and up and up until it reached the sky.

The funny looking man had told the truth after all.

The beanstalk stood quite close to Jack's window. Jack opened the window and climbed onto the beanstalk, which rose just like a big ladder.

Jack climbed and he climbed and he climbed and he climbed and he climbed and he climbed and he climbed, until at last he reached the sky. And when he got there he found a long broad road going as straight as an arrow. So he walked along and he walked along and he walked along until he came to a great big tall house, and on the doorstep there was a great big tall woman.

"Good morning, ma'am," said Jack, quite politely. "Could you be so kind as to give me some breakfast?" He hadn't had anything to eat the night before and was as hungry as could be.

"It's breakfast you want, is it?" said the great big tall woman. "It's breakfast you'll *be* if you don't move away from here. My husband is an ogre, and there's nothing he likes better than boys broiled on toast. You'd better go before he comes."

"Please, ma'am. I've had nothing to eat since yesterday morning," said Jack. "I may as well be broiled as die of hunger."

Well, the ogre's wife was not so bad after all. She took Jack into the kitchen and gave him a chunk of bread and a piece of cheese and a jug of milk. But Jack hadn't half finished these when—thump! thump! thump!—the whole house began to tremble with the noise of heavy footsteps.

"Goodness gracious me! It's my old man," said the ogre's wife. "What on earth shall I do? Come along quick and jump in here." And she bundled Jack into the oven just as the ogre came in.

He was a big one, to be sure. At his belt he had three calves strung up by the heels, and he unhooked them and threw them down on the table and said, "Here, wife, broil me a couple of these for breakfast. Ah! what's this I smell?" He sniffed the air and then said,

> Fee—Fie—Fo—Fum,
> I smell the blood of an Englishman.
> Be he alive, or be he dead
> I'll grind his bones to make my bread.

"Nonsense, dear," said his wife, "you're dreaming. Or perhaps you smell the scraps of that little boy you liked so much for yesterday's dinner. Here, you go and wash up, and by the time you come back your breakfast will be ready."

So off the ogre went, and Jack was just going to jump out of the oven and run away when the woman told him not to budge.

"Wait until he's asleep," she said. "He always has a doze after breakfast."

The ogre ate his breakfast. Then he went to a big chest and took out a couple of bags of gold coins. Then down he sat and counted them until at last his head began to nod and he started to snore, and the whole house began to shake again.

Then Jack crept out on tiptoe from the oven, and as he was passing the ogre he took one of the bags of gold under his arm, and off he ran until he got to the beanstalk. Then he threw down the bag of gold, which fell all the way down to his mother's garden. Then he climbed down and climbed down and climbed down until at last he got home and told his Mother of his adventure, and showed her the gold.

"Well, Mother," Jack said, "wasn't I right about the beans? They are really magical, you see."

The bag of gold kept them well fed and clothed for some time, but at last it ran out. Jack decided to try his luck once more up at the top of the beanstalk. So one fine morning he rose up early, and got onto the beanstalk, and he climbed and he climbed and he climbed and he climbed and he climbed and he climbed until at last he came out onto the road again and up to the great big tall house he had been to before. There, sure enough, was the great big tall woman standing on the doorstep.

"Good morning, ma'am," said Jack, as bold as brass. "Could you be so good as to give me something to eat?"

"Go away, my boy," said the big tall woman, "or else my husband will eat you up for breakfast. But aren't you the youngster who came here once before? Do you know, that very day my old man surely missed one of

his bags of gold."

"That's strange, ma'am," said Jack. "I dare say I could tell you something about that, but I'm so hungry I can't speak until I've had something to eat."

Well the big tall woman was so curious that she took him in and gave him something to eat. But he had scarcely begun munching it as slowly as he could when—thump! thump! thump!—they heard the ogre's footsteps, and his wife hid Jack away in the oven.

In came the ogre, who said, "Fee—Fie—Fo—Fum," and then had a breakfast of three broiled oxen. Then he said, "Wife, bring me the hen that lays the golden eggs." So she brought it, and the ogre said, "Lay." And the hen laid an egg all of gold. And then the ogre began to nod his head, and to snore until the house shook.

Jack crept out of the oven on tiptoe and grabbed the golden hen, and was off before you could say "Jack Robinson." But the hen gave a loud cackle and woke the ogre. Just as Jack got out of the house, he heard the ogre calling, "Wife, wife, where is my hen?"

Jack rushed off to the beanstalk and went down as fast as he could. When he got home he showed his Mother the wonderful hen, and said "Lay" to it, and it laid a solid gold egg.

Well, Jack was not content, and it wasn't very long before he wanted to have another try at his luck up there at the top of the beanstalk. So one fine morning, he rose up early and got onto the beanstalk, and he climbed and he climbed and he climbed and he climbed until he got to the top.

This time he knew better than to go straight to the ogre's house. When he got near it, he hid behind a bush until he saw the ogre's wife come out with a pail to get some water from the well. Then he slipped into the house and climbed into a large cooking pot. He hadn't been there long when he heard—thump! thump! thump!—as before, and in came the ogre and his wife.

Fee—Fie—Fo—Fum

I smell the blood of an Englishman, cried the ogre. "I smell him, wife, I smell him."

"Do you, my dearie?" said the ogre's wife. "Then, if it's that little rogue that stole your gold and the hen that laid the golden eggs, he's sure to have gotten into the oven." And they both rushed to the oven. But Jack wasn't there, luckily, and the ogre's wife said, "There you go again, you and your Fee—Fie—Fo—Fum. Why, of course, it's the boy you caught last night that I've just broiled for your breakfast that you smell. How forgetful I am, and how careless you are not to know the difference between alive and dead after all these years."

So the ogre sat down to breakfast, but now and then he would mutter, "Well, I could have sworn . . ." and then he would get up and search the pantry and cupboards and everything. Only, luckily, he didn't think of looking in the large cooking pot.

After breakfast was over, the ogre called out, "Wife, wife, bring me my golden harp." So she brought it and put it on the table before him. Then he said, "Sing!" and the golden harp sang most beautifully. And it went on singing until the ogre fell asleep and commenced to snore like thunder.

Then Jack lifted up the lid of the cooking pot very quietly and got down like a mouse and crept on hands and knees until he came to the table. Then up he reached, caught hold of the golden harp, and dashed with it toward the door. But the harp called out quite loud, "Master! Master!" and the ogre woke up just in time to see Jack running off with his harp.

Jack ran as fast as he could, and the ogre came rushing after, and would soon have caught him except for Jack's having a head start and knowing just where he was going. When he got to the beanstalk the ogre was not more than 20 yards behind. Then Jack suddenly seemed to disappear, and when the ogre came to the end of the road he looked down to see Jack climbing down the beanstalk for dear life.

The harp cried out again, "Master! Master!" and the ogre swung down onto the beanstalk, which shook with his weight, and began climbing down after Jack.

Jack climbed down and climbed down and climbed down until he was very nearly home. Then he called out, "Mother! Mother! Bring me my axe, bring me my axe!" And his Mother came rushing out with the axe in her hand. But when she got to the beanstalk she stood stock-still with fright, for there she saw the ogre with his legs just through the clouds.

Jack jumped down and got hold of the axe and gave a chop at the beanstalk that cut it halfway through. The ogre felt the beanstalk shake and quiver, so he stopped to see what was the matter. Then Jack gave another chop with the axe, and the beanstalk was cut in two and began to topple over. The ogre fell down with a crash and was killed.

Then Jack showed his Mother the golden harp and commanded it to sing, and it sang most beautifully.

The magic harp brought them fame, and the goose that laid golden eggs made them rich. Jack married a beautiful princess, and they all lived happily ever after.

Here is a chapter from one of the best loved children's books of all time, Winnie-the-Pooh. *In this adventure, Pooh's appetite for honey gets him into some pretty serious trouble. Luckily for Pooh, Christopher Robin always seems to know what should be done. Friends like Christopher Robin are good to have around.*

From Winnie-the-Pooh

A. A. Milne

IN WHICH *Pooh Goes Visiting and Gets Into a Tight Place*

EDWARD BEAR, known to his friends as Winnie-the-Pooh, or Pooh for short, was walking through the forest one day, humming proudly to himself. He had made up a little hum that very morning, as he was doing his Stoutness Exercises in front of the glass: *Tra-la-la, tra-la-la,* as he stretched up as high as he could go, and then *Tra-la-la, tra-la-oh, help!-la,* as he tried to reach his toes. After breakfast he had said it over and over to himself until he had learnt it off by heart, and now he was humming it right through properly. It went like this:

> *Tra-la-la, tra-la-la,*
> *Tra-la-la, tra-la-la,*
> *Rum-tum-tiddle-um-tum.*
> *Tiddle-iddle, tiddle-iddle,*
> *Tiddle-iddle, tiddle-iddle,*
> *Rum-tum-tum-tiddle-um.*

Well, he was humming this hum to himself, and walking along gaily, wondering what everybody else was doing, and what it felt like, being somebody else, when suddenly he came to a sandy bank, and in the bank was a large hole.

"Aha!" said Pooh. *(Rum-tum-tiddle-um-tum.)* "If I know anything about anything, that hole means Rabbit," he said, "and Rabbit means Company," he said, "and Company means Food and Listening-to-Me-Humming and such like. *Rum-tum-tum-tiddle-um.*"

So he bent down, put his head into the hole, and called out:

"Is anybody at home?"

There was a sudden scuffling noise from inside the hole, and then silence.

"What I said was, 'Is anybody at home?'" called out Pooh very loudly.

"No!" said a voice; and then added, "You needn't shout so loud. I heard you quite well the first time."

"Bother!" said Pooh. "Isn't there anybody here at all?"

"Nobody."

Winnie-the-Pooh took his head out of the hole, and thought for a little, and he thought to himself, "There must be somebody there, because somebody must have *said* 'Nobody.'" So he put his head back in the hole, and said:

"Hallo, Rabbit, isn't that you?"

"No," said Rabbit, in a different sort of voice this time.

"But isn't that Rabbit's voice?"

"I don't *think* so," said Rabbit. "It isn't *meant* to be."

"Oh!" said Pooh.

He took his head out of the hole, and had another think, and then he put it back, and said:

"Well, could you very kindly tell me where Rabbit is?"

"He has gone to see his friend Pooh Bear, who is a great friend of his."

"But this *is* Me! said Bear, very much surprised.

"What sort of Me?"

"Pooh Bear."

"Are you sure?" said Rabbit, still more surprised.

"Quite, quite sure," said Pooh.

"Oh, well, then, come in."

So Pooh pushed and pushed and pushed his way through the hole, and at last he got in.

"You were quite right," said Rabbit, looking at him all over. "It *is* you. Glad to see you."

"Who did you think it was?"

"Well, I wasn't sure. You know how it is in the Forest. One can't have *anybody* coming into one's house. One has to be *careful*. What about a mouthful of something?"

Pooh always liked a little something at eleven o'clock in the morning, and he was very glad to see Rabbit getting out the plates and mugs; and when Rabbit said, "Honey or condensed milk with your bread?" he was so excited that he said, "Both," and then, so as not to seem greedy, he added, "But don't bother about the bread, please." And for a long time after that he said nothing . . . until at last, humming to himself in a rather sticky voice, he got up, shook Rabbit lovingly by the paw, and said that he must be going on.

"Must you?" said Rabbit politely.

"Well," said Pooh, "I could stay a little longer if it—if you—" and he tried very hard to look in the direction of the larder.

"As a matter of fact," said Rabbit, "I was going out myself directly."

"Oh, well, then, I'll be going on. Good-bye."

"Well, good-bye, if you're sure you won't have any more."

"*Is* there any more?" asked Pooh quickly.

Rabbit took the covers off the dishes, and said, "No, there wasn't."

"I thought not," said Pooh, nodding to himself. "Well, good-bye. I must be going on."

So he started to climb out of the hole. He pulled with his front paws, and pushed with his back paws, and in a little while his nose was out in the open again . . . and then his ears . . . and then his front paws . . . and then his shoulders . . . and then—

"Oh, help!" said Pooh. "I'd better go back."

"Oh, bother!" said Pooh. "I shall have to go on."

"I can't do either!" said Pooh. "Oh, help *and* bother!"

Now by this time Rabbit wanted to go for a walk too, and finding the front door full, he went out by the back door, and came round to Pooh, and looked at him.

"Hallo, are you stuck?" he asked.

"N-no," said Pooh carelessly. "Just resting and thinking and humming to myself."

"Here, give us a paw."

Pooh Bear stretched out a paw, and Rabbit pulled and pulled and pulled. . . .

"Ow!" cried Pooh. "You're hurting!"

"The fact is," said Rabbit, "you're stuck."

"It all comes," said Pooh crossly, "of not having front doors big enough."

"It all comes," said Rabbit sternly, "of eating too much. I thought at the time," said Rabbit, "only I didn't like to say anything," said Rabbit, "that one of us was eating too much," said Rabbit, "and I knew it wasn't *me*," he said. "Well, well, I shall go and fetch Christoper Robin."

Christopher Robin lived at the other end of the Forest, and when he came back with Rabbit, and saw the front half of Pooh, he said, "Silly old Bear," in such a loving voice that everybody felt quite hopeful again.

"I was just beginning to think," said Bear, sniffing slightly, "that Rabbit might never be able to use his front door again. And I should *hate* that," he said.

"So should I," said Rabbit.

"Use his front door again?" said Christopher Robin. "Of course he'll use his front door again."

"Good," said Rabbit.

"If we can't pull you out, Pooh, we might push you back."

Rabbit scratched his whiskers thoughtfully, and pointed out that, when once Pooh was pushed back, he was back, and of course nobody was more glad to see Pooh than *he* was, still there it was, some lived in trees and some lived underground, and—

"You mean I'd *never* get out?" said Pooh.

"I mean," said Rabbit, "that having got *so* far, it seems a pity to waste it."

Christopher Robin nodded.

"Then there's only one thing to be done," he said.

"We shall have to wait for you to get thin again."

"How long does getting thin take?" asked Pooh anxiously.

"About a week, I should think."

"But I can't stay here for a *week!*"

"You can *stay* here all right, silly old Bear. It's getting you out which is so difficult."

"We'll read to you," said Rabbit cheerfully. "And I hope it won't snow," he added. "And I say, old fellow, you're taking up a good deal of room in my house—*do* you mind if I use your back legs as a towel-horse? Because, I mean, there they are—doing nothing—and it would be very convenient just to hang the towels on them."

"A week!" said Pooh gloomily. *"What about meals?"*

"I'm afraid no meals," said Christopher Robin, "because of getting thin quicker. But we *will* read to you."

Bear began to sigh, and then found he couldn't because he was so tightly stuck; and a tear rolled down his eye, as he said:

"Then would you read a Sustaining Book, such as would help and comfort a Wedged Bear in Great Tightness?"

So for a week Christopher Robin read that sort of book at the North end of Pooh, and Rabbit hung his washing on the South end . . . and in between Bear felt himself getting slenderer and slenderer. And at the end of the week Christopher Robin said, *"Now!"*

So he took hold of Pooh's front paws and Rabbit took hold of Christopher Robin, and all Rabbit's friends and relations took hold of Rabbit, and they all pulled together. . . .

And for a long time Pooh only said *"Ow!"* . . .

And *"Oh!"* . . .

And then, all of a sudden, he said *"Pop!"* just as if a cork were coming out of a bottle.

And Christopher Robin and Rabbit and all Rabbit's friends and relations went head-over-heels backwards . . . and on the top of them came Winnie-the-Pooh—free!

So, with a nod of thanks to his friends, he went on with his walk through the forest, humming proudly to himself. But, Christopher Robin looked after him lovingly, and said to himself, "Silly old Bear!"

47

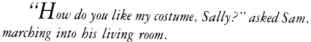

"How do you like my costume, Sally?" asked Sam, marching into his living room.

Sally looked up, and her eyes went wide.

"It looks great, Sam," she said. "You look just like a real colonial soldier. I bet you'll have the best costume in the whole school play."

"I don't know," Sam said thoughtfully. "Your country girl outfit looks good too."

"I can hardly wait, Sam," Sally said, standing up and imagining herself on the school stage.

"Ladies and gentleman, presenting our school dramatization of the classic folk story . . . Stone Soup!"

Stone Soup

Marcia Brown

THREE SOLDIERS trudged down a road in a strange country. They were on their way home from the wars. Besides being tired, they were hungry. In fact, they had eaten nothing for two days.

"How I would like a good dinner tonight," said the first.

"And a bed to sleep in," said the second.

"But all that is impossible," said the third. "We must march on."

On they marched. Suddenly, ahead of them they saw the lights of a village.

"Maybe we'll find a bite to eat there," said the first.

"And a loft to sleep in," said the second.

"No harm in asking," said the third.

Now the peasants of that place feared strangers. When they heard that three soldiers were coming down the road, they talked among themselves.

"Here come three soldiers. Soldiers are always hungry. But we have little enough for ourselves." And they hurried to hide their food.

They pushed sacks of barley under the hay in the lofts. They lowered buckets of milk down the wells.

They spread old quilts over the carrot bins. They hid their cabbages and potatoes under the beds. They hung their meat in the cellars.

They hid all they had to eat. Then—they waited.

The soldiers stopped first at the house of Paul and Françoise.

"Good evening to you," they said. "Could you spare a bit of food for three hungry soldiers?"

"We have had no food for ourselves for three days," said Paul. Françoise made a sad face. "It has been a poor harvest."

The three soldiers went on to the house of Albert and Louise.

"Could you spare a bit of food? And have you some corner where we could sleep for the night?"

"Oh no," said Albert. "We gave all we could spare to soldiers who came before you."

"Our beds are full," said Louise.

At Vincent and Marie's the answer was the same. It had been a poor harvest and all the grain must be kept for seed.

So it went all through the village. Not a peasant had any food to give away. They all had good reasons. One family had used the grain for feed. Another had an old sick father to care for. All had too many mouths to fill.

The villagers stood in the street and sighed. They looked as hungry as they could.

The three soldiers talked together.

Then the first soldier called out, "Good people!" The peasants drew near.

"We are three hungry soldiers in a strange land. We have asked you for food, and you have no food. Well then, we'll have to make stone soup."

The peasants stared.

Stone soup? That would be something to know about.

"First we'll need a large iron pot," the soldiers said.

The peasants brought the largest pot they could find. How else to cook enough?

"That's none too large," said the soldiers. "But it will do. And now, water to fill it and a fire to heat it."

It took many buckets of water to fill the pot. A fire was built on the village square and the pot was set to boil.

"And now, if you please, three round, smooth stones."

Those were easy enough to find.

The peasants' eyes grew round as they watched the soldiers drop the stones into the pot.

"Any soup needs salt and pepper," said the soldiers, as they began to stir.

Children ran to fetch salt and pepper.

"Stones like these generally make good soup. But oh, if there were carrots, it would be much better."

"Why, I think I have a carrot or two," said Françoise, and off she ran.

She came back with her apron full of carrots from the bin beneath the red quilt.

"A good stone soup should have cabbage," said the soldiers as they sliced the carrots into the pot. "But no use asking for what you don't have."

"I think I could find a cabbage somewhere," said Marie, and she hurried home. Back she came with three cabbages from the cupboard under the bed.

"If we only had a bit of beef and a few potatoes, this soup would be good enough for a rich man's table."

The peasants thought that over. They remembered their potatoes and the sides of beef hanging in the cellars. They ran to fetch them.

A rich man's soup—and all from a few stones. It seemed like magic!

"Ah," sighed the soldiers as they stirred in the beef and potatoes, "if we only had a little barley and a cup of milk! This soup would be fit for the king himself. Indeed he asked for just such a soup when last he dined with us."

The peasants looked at each other. The soldiers had

entertained the king! Well!

"But—no use asking for what you don't have," the soldiers sighed.

The peasants brought their barley from the lofts, they brought their milk from the wells. The soldiers stirred the barley and milk into the steaming broth while the peasants stared.

At last the soup was ready.

"All of you shall taste," the soldiers said. "But first a table must be set."

Great tables were placed in the square. And all around were lighted torches.

Such a soup! How good it smelled! Truly fit for a king.

But then the peasants asked themselves, "Would not such a soup require bread—and a roast—and cider?" Soon a banquet was spread and everyone sat down to eat.

Never had there been such a feast. Never had the peasants tasted such soup. And fancy, made from stones!

They ate and drank and ate and drank. And after that they danced.

They danced and sang far into the night.

At last they were tired. Then the three soldiers asked, "Is there not a loft where we could sleep?"

"Let three such wise and splendid gentlemen sleep in a loft? Indeed! They must have the best beds in the village."

So the first soldier slept in the priest's house.

The second soldier slept in the baker's house.

And the third soldier slept in the mayor's house.

In the morning the whole village gathered in the square to give them a send-off.

"Many thanks for what you have taught us," the peasants said to the soldiers. "We shall never go hungry, now that we know how to make soup from stones."

"Oh, it's all in knowing how," said the soldiers, and off they went down the road.

Everybody knows the story about Paul Revere and how, during the American Revolution, he rode his horse to warn the Minutemen that the British soldiers were coming. This famous poem by Henry Wadsworth Longfellow has been a favorite of readers young and old for more than a hundred years.

Paul Revere's Ride

Henry Wadsworth Longfellow

LISTEN, my children, and you shall hear
Of the midnight ride of Paul Revere,
On the eighteenth of April, in Seventy-five;
Hardly a man is now alive
Who remembers that famous day and year.

He said to his friend, "If the British march
By land or sea from the town tonight,
Hang a lantern aloft in the belfry arch
Of the North Church tower as a signal light,—
One, if by land, or two, if by sea;
And I on the opposite shore will be,
Ready to ride and spread the alarm
Through every Middlesex village and farm,
For the country folk to be up and to arm."

Then he said, "Good night!" and with muffled oar
Silently rowed to the Charlestown shore,
Just as the moon rose over the bay,
Where swinging wide at her moorings lay
The *Somerset*, British man-of-war;
A phantom ship, with each mast and spar
Across the moon like a prison bar,
And a huge black hulk, that was magnified
By its own reflection in the tide.

Meanwhile, his friend, through alley and street,
Wanders and watches with eager ears,
Till in silence around him he hears
The muster of men at the barrack door,
The sound of arms, and the tramp of feet,
And the measured tread of the grenadiers,
Marching down to their boats on the shore.

Then he climbed the tower of the Old North Church,
Up the wooden stairs, with stealthy tread,
To the belfry chamber overhead,
And startled the pigeons from their perch
On the somber rafters, that round him made
Masses and moving shapes of shade,—
Up the trembling ladder, steep and tall,
To the highest window in the wall,
Where he paused to listen and look down
A moment on the roofs of the town,
And the moonlight flowing over all.

Beneath, in the churchyard, lay the dead,
In their night-encampment on the hill,
Wrapped in silence so deep and still
That he could hear, like a sentinel's tread,
The watchful night wind, as it went
Creeping along from tent to tent,
And seeming to whisper, "All is well!"
A moment only he feels the spell
Of the place and the hour, and the secret dread
Of the lonely belfry and the dead;
For suddenly all his thoughts are bent
On a shadowy something far away,
Where the river widens to meet the bay,—
A line of black that bends and floats
On the rising tide, like a bridge of boats.

Meanwhile, impatient to mount and ride,
Booted and spurred, with a heavy stride
On the opposite shore walked Paul Revere.
Now he patted his horse's side,
Now gazed at the landscape far and near,
Then, impetuous, stamped the earth,
And turned and tightened his saddle-girth;
But mostly he watched with eager search
The belfry tower of the Old North Church,
As it rose above the graves on the hill,
Lonely and spectral and somber and still,
And lo! as he looks, on the belfry's height
A glimmer, and then a gleam of light!
He springs to the saddle, the bridle he turns,
But lingers and gazes, till full on his sight
A second lamp in the belfry burns!

A hurry of hoofs in a village street,
A shape in the moonlight, a bulk in the dark,
And beneath, from the pebbles, in passing, a spark
Struck out by a steed flying fearless and fleet:
That was all! And yet, through the gloom and the light,
The fate of a nation was riding that night;
And the spark struck out by that steed, in his flight,
Kindled the land into flame with its heat.

He has left the village and mounted the steep,
And beneath him, tranquil and broad and deep,
Is the Mystic, meeting the ocean tides;
And under the alders that skirt its edge,
Now soft on the sand, now loud on the ledge,
Is heard the tramp of his steed as he rides.

It was twelve by the village clock
When he crossed the bridge into Medford town.
He heard the crowing of the cock,
And the barking of the farmer's dog,
And felt the damp of the river fog,
That rises after the sun goes down.

It was one by the village clock,
When he galloped into Lexington.
He saw the gilded weathercock
Swim in the moonlight as he passed,
And the meetinghouse windows, blank and bare,
Gaze at him with a spectral glare,
As if they already stood aghast
At the bloody work they would look upon.

55

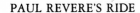

It was two by the village clock,
When he came to the bridge in Concord town.
He heard the bleating of the flock,
And the twitter of birds among the trees,
And felt the breath of the morning breeze
Blowing over the meadows brown.
And one was safe and asleep in his bed
Who at the bridge would be first to fall,
Who that day would be lying dead,
Pierced by a British musketball.

You know the rest. In the books you have read,
How the British Regulars fired and fled,—
How the farmers gave them ball for ball,
From behind each fence and farmyard wall,
Chasing the redcoats down the lane,
Then crossing the fields to emerge again
Under the trees at the turn of the road,
And only pausing to fire and load.

So through the night rode Paul Revere;
And so through the night went his cry of alarm
To every Middlesex village and farm,—
A cry of defiance and not of fear,
A voice in the darkness, a knock at the door,
And a word that shall echo forevermore!
For, borne on the night wind of the Past,
Through all our history, to the last,
In the hour of darkness and peril and need,
The people will waken and listen to hear
The hurrying hoofbeats of that steed,
And the midnight message of Paul Revere.

This is a beautiful folk tale from Japan. It is a simple story of a poor farmer who rescues a helpless bird, a crane, from certain death and soon after marries a beautiful but mysterious young woman. It is perhaps the most popular folk tale in Japan, and many have seen it presented in play and movie form.

The Crane Wife

Retold by Sumiko Yagawa

IN A FARAWAY MOUNTAIN VILLAGE, where the snow falls deep and white, there once lived all alone a poor young peasant named Yohei. One day, at the beginning of winter, Yohei went out into the snow to run an errand, and, as he hurried home, suddenly *xasaxasa* he heard a rustling sound. It was a crane, dragging its wing, as it swooped down and landed on the path. Now Yohei could see that the bird was in great pain, for an arrow had pierced its wing. He went to where the crane lay, drew out the arrow, and very carefully tended its wound.

Late that night there came a tapping *hotohoto* on the door of Yohei's hut. It seemed very peculiar for someone to be calling at that time of night. When he slid open the door to look out, there before him stood a beautiful young woman.

"I beg you, sir," she said in a voice both delicate and refined, "please allow me to become your wife."

Yohei could hardly believe his ears. The more closely he looked, the more noble and lovely the woman appeared. Gently he took her hand and brought her inside.

"Yohei has got some fine wife at his house," the

villagers gossiped among themselves.

And it was true. The young woman was modest and kind, and she served Yohei faithfully. He could no longer recognize the cold, cold dreary hut where he had lived all alone, his house had become so bright and warm. The simple Yohei was happier than he could have ever dreamed.

In reality, however, with two mouths to feed instead of one, poor Yohei became poorer than he was before. And, since it was winter and there was no work to be found, he was very quickly coming to the bottom of what he had stored away.

At this point the young woman had a suggestion. "The other women of the village have looms upon which to weave cloth," she said. "If you would be so kind as to allow it, I should like to try my hand at weaving too."

In the back room of the hut, the young woman set up a loom and closed it off with sliding paper doors. Then she said to Yohei, "Please, I beg you, I beg you never look in upon me while I am weaving."

Tonkara tonkara. For three days and three nights the sound of the loom continued. Without stopping either to eat or drink, the young woman went on weaving and weaving. Finally, on the fourth day, she came out. To Yohei she seemed strangely thin and completely exhausted as, without a word, she held out to him a bolt of material.

And such exquisite cloth it was! Even Yohei, who had absolutely no knowledge of woven goods, could only stare in astonishment at the elegant, silken fabric.

Yohei took the cloth and set out for town. There he was able to sell it for such a high price that for a while the two of them had enough money to live quite comfortably and pleasantly.

The winter, however, stretched on and on until, finally, there was very little money left. Yohei hesitated to say anything, so he kept quiet, but at last the young

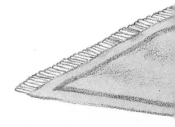

woman spoke up. "I shall weave on the loom one more time. But, please, let this be the last." And, once more, having been warned not to look in on the woman as she wove, the simple Yohei settled down to wait outside just as she asked.

This time the weaving took four days and four nights. A second time the young woman appeared carrying a bolt of cloth, but now she seemed thinner and more pathetic than before. The fabric, moreover, was lighter and even more beautiful. It seemed almost to glow with a light all its own.

Yohei sold the material for an even higher price than the first time. "My," he marveled, "what a good wife I have!" The money bag he carried was heavy, but Yohei's heart was light, and he fairly skipped as he hurried home.

Now the man next door had noticed that Yohei seemed to be living far more grandly than he had in the old days, and he was most curious. Pretending to be very casual about it all, he made his way through the snow and began to chat. Yohei, being a simple and innocent fellow, told the neighbor how his wife's woven goods had brought a wonderful price.

The man became more curious than ever. "Tell me," he said, "just what kind of thread does your wife use? My woman's cotton cloth never fetched a price like that. If your wife's stuff is as marvelous as you say, you ought to take it to the capital, to the home of some noble. You could probably sell it for ten times, for a hundred times more. Say, how about it? Why don't you let me do it for you? We'd split the profits right down the middle. Just think of it! We could live out the rest of our lives doing nothing but sitting back and fanning ourselves."

Before Yohei's very eyes, gold coins great and small began to dazzle and dance. If only he could get his wife to relent, if only he could persuade her to weave again, they could seize such a fortune as had never been known before.

When Yohei presented her with this idea, the young woman seemed quite perplexed. "Why in the world," she asked, "would anyone need so much money as that?"

"Don't you see?" he answered. "With money like that a man's problems would all disappear. He could buy anything he liked. He could even start his own business."

"Isn't it plenty to be able to live together, just the two of us?"

When she spoke this way, Yohei could say no more. However, from that time on, whether asleep or awake, all he could do was think about money. It was so painful for the young woman to see Yohei in this state that her eyes filled with tears as she watched him, until finally, unable to bear it another day, she bowed to his will.

"Very well then," she said. "I will weave one more time. But truly, after this, I must never weave again." And once more she warned the now joyful Yohei, saying, "For the sake of heaven, remember. Do not look in on me."

Yohei rubbed his hands together in his eagerness and sat down to wait.

Tonkara tonkara. The sound of the loom continued on and on into the fifth day. The work in the back room seemed to be taking longer than ever.

Yohei, no longer the simple fellow that he had once been, began to wonder about certain peculiar things. Why did the young woman appear to grow thinner every time she wove? What was going on in there behind those paper doors? How could she weave such beautiful cloth when she never seemed to buy any thread?

The longer he had to wait, the more he yearned to peep into the room until, at last, he put his hand upon the door.

"Ah!" came a voice from within. At the same time Yohei cried out in horror and fell back from the doorway.

What Yohei saw was not human. It was a crane, smeared with blood, for with its beak it had plucked out its own feathers to place them in the loom.

At the sight Yohei collapsed into a deep faint.

When he came to himself, he found, lying near his hand, a bolt of fabric, pure and radiantly white, through which was woven a thread of bright crimson. It shone with a light this world has never known.

From somewhere Yohei heard the whisper of a delicate, familiar voice. "I had hoped," the voice said sorrowfully, "you would be able to honor my entreaty. But because you looked upon me in my suffering, I can no longer tarry in the human world. I am the crane you saved on the snowy path. I fell in love with your gentle, simple heart, and, trusting it alone, I came to live by your side. I pray that your life will be long and that you will always be happy."

"Wai-t!" Yohei stumbled in his haste to get outside.

It was nearly spring, and, over the crest of the distant mountains, he could barely discern the tiny form of a single crane, flying farther and farther away.

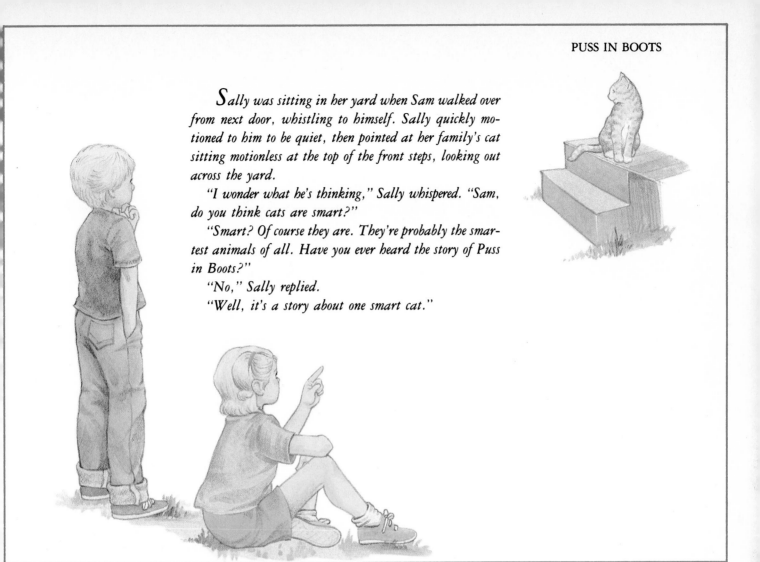

Sally was sitting in her yard when Sam walked over from next door, whistling to himself. Sally quickly motioned to him to be quiet, then pointed at her family's cat sitting motionless at the top of the front steps, looking out across the yard.

"I wonder what he's thinking," Sally whispered. "Sam, do you think cats are smart?"

"Smart? Of course they are. They're probably the smartest animals of all. Have you ever heard the story of Puss in Boots?"

"No," Sally replied.

"Well, it's a story about one smart cat."

Puss in Boots

Retold by Eleanor Graham Vance

THERE WAS ONCE A MILLER who had nothing to leave to his three sons but his mill, his ass, and his cat. The division was soon made. The eldest had the mill, the second the ass, and the youngest nothing but the cat.

The poor young fellow was quite sad at his lot.

"My brothers," said he, "may make a good living by joining together, but as for me, when I have eaten the cat and made a muff of his fur, I must die of hunger."

The cat, who heard all this, said to him, "Do not worry, my good master. Just give me a bag, and let me have a pair of high boots made for me so that I can scamper among the brambles, and you shall see that you are not so badly off as you imagine."

Though the cat's master did not build very much on what he said, he gave Puss what he asked for. The cat pulled on the boots and, putting his bag around his neck, with some bran in it, he went into a meadow

where many rabbits lived. There he stretched out as if he were dead. Almost at once a rash and foolish young rabbit came along and jumped into his bag.

Master Puss, immediately drawing the strings, took his prey to the palace and asked to speak to his majesty.

He was shown upstairs into the king's apartment. Making a low bow, he said, "I have brought you, sir, a gift from my noble lord the Marquis of Carabas" (for that was the title which Puss was pleased to give his master).

"Tell your master," said the king, "that I thank him."

Another time Puss hid among some standing corn, holding his bag open, and when a brace of fine partridges ran into it, he again drew the strings. And again he made a present of game to the king. The king received the partridges with great pleasure and sent his greetings once more to the unknown marquis.

The cat continued for two or three months to carry to His Majesty presents of game from his master.

Then one day when he knew the king was to take the air along the riverside with his daughter, the most beautiful princess in the world, he said to his master, "If you will follow my advice, your fortune is made. You have only to bathe in the river where I show you, and leave the rest to me."

The Marquis of Carabas did what the cat advised him to, without knowing why or wherefore.

While he was bathing, the king passed by, and the cat began to cry as loud as he could, "Help, help, my master the Marquis of Carabas is drowning!"

At this the king put his head out of his coach window and quickly commanded his guards to run to the assistance of the Marquis of Carabas. They soon fished the astonished marquis out of the river.

Meanwhile the cat had hidden his master's shabby clothes under a big stone. Now he came running up to the king's coach, saying, "Rogues have made off with my master's clothes!"

The king immediately commanded the officers of his wardrobe to run and fetch one of his handsomest costumes for the lord Marquis of Carabas.

Dressed in the fine clothes, the young man looked very handsome indeed, and the king's daughter was secretly attracted to him. The Marquis of Carabas had no sooner cast two or three respectful and tender glances at her than she fell desperately in love with him. The king, not noticing this, invited the young man into the coach to join them on their airing.

The cat, overjoyed to see his project succeeding, marched on ahead. Meeting some countrymen who were mowing a meadow, he said to them, "Good people, if you do not tell the king that this meadow belongs to the Marquis of Carabas, you shall be chopped up as fine as herbs for the pot."

So when the king asked whose meadows they were, the mowers replied, "The Marquis of Carabas."

The master cat, who still went on before, met some reapers and said to them, "Good people, if you do not tell the king that this corn field belongs to the Marquis of Carabas, you shall be chopped up as fine as herbs for the pot."

The king soon asked to whom all the corn belonged. "To the Marquis of Carabas," replied the reapers.

The master cat, going on before, said the same thing to all he met, and the king was astonished at the vast estates of the Marquis of Carabas.

Master Puss came at last to the great castle where lived the powerful ogre to whom all these lands really belonged. The cat asked to speak with him, to pay his respects, and the ogre received him as civilly as an ogre could.

"I have been told," said the cat, "that you are able to change yourself into any creature you choose."

"This is true," said the ogre briskly. "You shall now see me become a lion."

Puss was so terrified at seeing a fierce lion near him

that he scampered up onto the rafters. When the ogre resumed his natural shape, he came back down.

"I have moreover been informed," said the cat, "that you can change yourself into the smallest animals—a mouse or rat. But I must say I consider this impossible."

"Impossible?" cried the ogre. "You shall see!" And he changed himself into a tiny mouse and began to run about the floor.

Puss promptly fell upon him and ate him up.

Meanwhile the king was passing the castle. Puss ran out and said to the king, "Your Majesty is welcome to the castle of my lord Marquis of Carabas."

"What, my lord Marquis?" cried the king. "Is this castle yours, also? What could be finer! Let us go into it, if you please."

The marquis gave his hand to the princess, and they followed the king. They passed into a spacious hall where they found a fine feast which the ogre had prepared for some of his wicked friends, who dared not enter now.

His Majesty was perfectly charmed with the marquis and his vast estates, as was the princess. "It will be your own fault, my lord Marquis," said the king, "if you are not my son-in-law."

The marquis, bowing low, accepted the honor and married the happy princess that very day.

And Puss became a great lord who hunted mice, after that, only as a sport.

Here is another favorite fairy tale. The story of Cinderella is in many ways like the story of Snow White. Each concerns a good and beautiful girl who suffers because of a wicked stepmother. This tale also involves magic, a good deal of it, courtesy of Cinderella's fairy godmother.

Cinderella

Retold by Eleanor Graham Vance

ONCE THERE WAS a gentleman who married for his second wife the most haughty and disagreeable woman you could imagine. She had two daughters who were just like her in every way. The gentleman's own daughter, by his first wife, was a girl who for goodness and sweetness of disposition was the best in the world.

The stepmother could not bear this pretty girl and her goodness, so she made her do all the meanest work of the house. She scoured the dishes, tables, and floors, and dusted the bedchambers. She slept in a garret while her stepsisters had fine rooms with inlaid floors, and glittering looking glasses so large that they could see themselves from head to foot.

The poor girl bore all this patiently, and when her work was done she used to go into the chimney corner and sit among the ashes. So her stepsisters sneeringly called her Cinderella.

Now it happened that the king's son gave a ball and invited all persons of fashion to it. The stepsisters were invited, and they were mightily pleased at this invitation. Soon they were busy choosing their most becoming gowns, petticoats, and headdresses. This meant more work for Cinderella, for she ironed her sisters' ruffles and brushed their gowns.

"For my part," said the elder, "I will wear my red velvet suit."

"And I," said the younger, "shall ornament my old skirt and my gold-flowered cloak with my diamond stomacher."

Cinderella was called upon to dress their hair and apply their beauty patches, and she did it all perfectly.

As she worked they said to her, "Cinderella, would you not like to be going, too? Oh, how everyone would laugh to see a cinder maid at the prince's ball!"

Cinderella did not reply, but when they left for court she followed them with her eyes as far as she could. When she lost sight of them, she went back to the chimney corner and there fell to crying.

"What is the matter?" asked a soft voice.

Cinderella looked up and saw her fairy godmother before her.

But Cinderella could not speak for sobbing.

"You wish to go to the ball, is that it?"

Cinderella nodded.

"Well," said her godmother, "be a good girl and I shall arrange it. First run into the garden and bring me a pumpkin."

Cinderella quickly brought the best one she could find, wondering how it could help. Her godmother scooped out all the inside, then struck it with her wand. Instantly the pumpkin was turned into a splendid golden coach.

Next she ordered Cinderella to lift the little trap door of the kitchen mousetrap, in which were six live mice and a rat. She gave each mouse a tap with her wand as it came out, and instantly each one was changed into a handsome, dapple-gray horse. And the fine, fat rat, at the touch of her wand, became a fat, jolly coachman.

"Now look in the garden once more," she ordered. "You will find six lizards behind the watering pot. Bring them to me."

Cinderella had no sooner done so than they became six footmen in gold and silver liveries, who skipped up behind the coach as if they had been doing it all their lives.

"Well," said the fairy to Cinderella, "are you not pleased with your equipage for the ball?"

"Oh, yes," she cried, "but must I go in these rags?"

The godmother touched her with the wand, and instantly her clothes were turned into cloth of gold and silver, set with jewels. Finally Cinderella was given a pair of glass slippers, quite the prettiest in the world.

"Now have a good time," said the fairy, as the footmen helped Cinderella into the coach. "But there is one thing you must remember; you must leave by midnight, for the magic will last no longer. At twelve o'clock your coach will turn back into a pumpkin, your servants into lizards and rats, and your clothes will be rags once more."

"I shall remember," said Cinderella.

Then she drove away, scarcely able to contain herself for joy.

The king's son, told that a great princess whom no one knew had come, ran out to receive her, and led her into the hall. The music stopped and voices died away as she entered at the prince's side.

"Who is the lovely princess? Who is the lovely princess?" The question was whispered over and over again around the ballroom. The king himself asked it, and told the queen it was a long time since he had seen so beautiful and lovely a creature.

The king's son led her out to dance, and she danced so gracefully that everyone admired her still more.

When the fine supper was served, the prince ate not a mouthful, so intent was he upon the lovely creature beside him. Even Cinderella's sisters were charmed by the beautiful princess when she spoke to them. For they did not recognize her as their own sister.

The evening passed gaily. But when the palace clock struck eleven and three quarters, Cinderella remembered. Rising from her seat, she curtsied to the company and hastened away.

When her sisters came home, Cinderella, dressed again in her old rags, rubbed her eyes and yawned as if she had been asleep for hours.

"Wake up, Cinderella, and help us get undressed," they said.

Then they told her about the ball, and the beautiful
princess whom no one knew, and how she had sought
them out and showed them courtesies.

"The king's son," they said, "would give all the world
to know who she is. He is giving another ball tomorrow
night so that he may see her again."

Cinderella, hiding her joy, seemed not interested.
But at the first opportunity she sought out her godmother and thanked her, and said she most heartily
wished to go again the next night.

The next night the two sisters were at the ball, and
so was Cinderella, but dressed even more magnificently
than before. The king's son was always at her side, and
she fell so deeply in love with him that she quite forgot
about the time. When the palace clock began to strike,
she thought it could be no more than eleven, but she
counted the strokes—ten, eleven, twelve!

Away ran Cinderella, as nimble as a deer.

The prince followed, but could not overtake her. On
the palace steps, however, she lost one of her dainty
little glass slippers, which the prince picked up most
carefully. He asked the guards at the palace gate if they
had seen a princess go out, but they said they had seen
no one but a young girl, very poorly dressed. So the
prince returned sadly to the palace.

Cinderella got home safely, but quite out of breath,
without coach or footmen, and in her old rags. She had
nothing left of all her finery but the other of the little
glass slippers.

When the two sisters returned from the ball, they had more to say of the beautiful princess. "She ran away at the stroke of twelve," they said, "in so much haste that she dropped one of her little glass slippers, the prettiest in all the world. The king's son has the slipper, and is certainly very much in love with its owner."

What they said was true. A very few days later the king's son sent out royal trumpeters to proclaim that he would marry whomever the slipper would fit. It was tried on all the princesses and the duchesses and the ladies of the court, but in vain.

Presently the prince came to the house where Cinderella lived. The two sisters tried their best to thrust a foot into the slipper, but they could not. Then the prince asked Cinderella to try.

"She is too dirty!" cried the stepmother, and Cinderella's sisters burst out laughing.

But the prince looked at Cinderella and saw that she was very lovely. He asked her to sit down.

When he held up the slipper, her foot went in very easily, and it fitted as smoothly as wax.

The sisters were amazed, but still more so when Cinderella pulled out of her apron pocket the other slipper and put it on. Then in came the fairy godmother, who touched with her wand Cinderella's clothes, making them richer and more magnificent than ever before.

"Yes, you are my princess!" cried the prince. "I beg of you, be my bride!"

Now her two sisters recognized her as the beautiful lady indeed. They hastily begged her pardon for their ill treatment of her.

"Of course I forgive you," said Cinderella.

Then the happy prince led Cinderella to his royal carriage, and away they went to the palace. A few days later they were married.

And Cinderella, who was no less good than she was beautiful, forgave her stepsisters and they all lived happily ever after.

This fairy tale concerns a girl who performs an act of kindness and gains an unwelcome companion. But she is no ordinary girl—she is a princess. And her new friend is not ordinary either. Read on. . . .

The Frog Prince

Jacob and Wilhelm Grimm

IN THE OLDEN TIME, when wishing was having, there lived a King whose daughters were all beautiful. But the youngest was so exceedingly beautiful that the sun himself was enchanted every time she came out into the sunshine.

Near the castle of this King was a large and gloomy forest, and in the midst stood an old lime tree, beneath whose branches splashed a little fountain. So whenever it was very hot, the King's youngest daughter ran off into this wood, and sat down by the side of this fountain. When she was bored, she would often divert herself by throwing a golden ball up in the air and catching it. And this was her favorite amusement.

Now one day it happened that when the Princess threw this golden ball into the air, it did not fall down into her hand, but on the grass. Then it rolled past her into the fountain. The King's daughter followed the ball with her eyes, but it disappeared beneath the water, which was so deep that no one could see to the bottom. She began to cry louder and louder. As she cried, a voice called out, "Why weepest thou, O King's daughter? Thy tears would melt even a stone to pity." And she looked around to the spot whence the voice came, and saw a frog stretching his thick ugly head out of the water.

"You old water-paddler," said she, "was it you that spoke? I am weeping for my golden ball which has slipped away from me into the water."

"Be quiet and do not cry," answered the Frog. "I can give thee good advice. But what wilt thou give me if I fetch thy plaything up again?"

"What will you have, dear Frog?" said she. "My dresses, my pearls and jewels, or the golden crown which I wear?"

The Frog answered, "Dresses, or jewels, or golden crowns are not for me. But if thou wilt love me, and let me be thy companion and playfellow, and sit at thy table, and eat from thy little golden plate, and drink out of thy cup, and sleep in thy little bed—if thou wilt promise me all these, then will I dive down and fetch up thy golden ball."

"Oh, I will promise you all," said she, "if only you will get me my ball." But she thought to herself, "What is the silly Frog chattering about? Let him remain in the water with his equals. He cannot mix in society."

But the Frog, as soon as he had received her promise, drew his head under the water and dived down. Presently he swam up again with the ball in his mouth, and threw it on the grass. The King's daughter was full of joy when she again saw her beautiful plaything. Taking it up, she ran off immediately.

"Stop! stop!" cried the Frog. "Take me with thee. I can't run as thou canst." But his croaking was useless. Although it was loud enough, the King's daughter did not hear it. Hastening home, she soon forgot the poor Frog, who was obliged to leap back into the fountain.

The next day, when the King's daughter was sitting at table with her father and all his courtiers, and was eating from her own little golden plate, something was heard coming up the marble stairs, *splish-splash, splish-splash.* When it arrived at the top, it knocked at the door, and a voice said, "Open the door, thou youngest daughter of the King!"

She rose and went to see who it was that called her. But when she opened the door and caught sight of the Frog, she shut it again, and sat down at the table, looking very pale. But the King saw that her heart was beating violently, and asked her whether it were a giant who had come to fetch her away who stood at the door. "Oh, no!" she answered. "It is no giant, but an ugly Frog."

"What does the Frog want with you?" said the King.

"Oh, dear father, when I was sitting yesterday playing by the fountain, my golden ball fell into the water. This Frog fetched it up again because I cried so much, but first I must tell you, he pressed me so much, that I promised him he should be my companion. I never thought he could come out of the water, but somehow he has jumped out, and now he wants to come in here."

At that moment there was another knock, and a voice said:

> King's daughter, youngest,
> Open the door.
> Hast thou forgotten
> Thy promises made
> At the fountain so clear?
> 'Neath the lime-tree's shade?
> King's daughter, youngest,
> Open the door.

Then the King said, "What you have promised, that you must perform. Go and let him in." So the King's daughter went and opened the door. The Frog hopped in after her right up to her chair.

As soon as she was seated the Frog said, "Take me up." But she hesitated so long that at last the King ordered her to obey. And as soon as the Frog sat on the chair he jumped on to the table and said, "Now push thy plate near me, that we may eat together." And she did so, but as everyone saw, very unwillingly. The Frog seemed to relish his dinner much, but every bite that the King's daughter ate nearly choked her, till at last the Frog said, "I have satisfied my hunger and feel very tired. Wilt thou carry me upstairs now into thy chamber, so that we may go to sleep?" At this speech the King's daughter began to cry, for she was afraid of the cold Frog, and dared not touch him. Besides, he actually wanted to sleep on her own beautiful, clean bed.

But her tears only made the King angry. He said, "He helped you in the time of your trouble, and must not now be despised!"

So she took the Frog up with two fingers, and put him in a corner of her chamber. But as she lay in her bed, he crept up to it, and said, "I am so very tired that I shall sleep well. Do take me up or I will tell thy father."

This speech made the King's daughter terribly angry. Catching the Frog up, she threw him with all her strength against the wall, saying, "Now will you be quiet, you ugly Frog!"

But as he fell he was changed from a frog into a handsome Prince with beautiful eyes. After a little while, he became, with her father's consent, her dear companion and betrothed. Then he told her how he had been transformed by an evil witch, and that no one but herself could have had the power to take him out of the fountain. And soon they were married and went together into the Prince's own kingdom.

Hans Christian Andersen was one of the greatest storytellers the world has ever known. His stories have been translated into many languages and have been enjoyed by countless readers for generations. This tale, perhaps his most popular, deals with something we all experience sooner or later, the hurt of not being accepted as we are, of being left out because we are different.

The Ugly Duckling

Hans Christian Andersen

IT WAS SO BEAUTIFUL out in the country. It was summer. The oats were still green, but the wheat was turning yellow. Down in the meadow the grass had been cut and made into haystacks; and there the storks walked on their long red legs talking Egyptian, because that was the language they had been taught by their mothers. The fields were enclosed by woods, and hidden among them were little lakes and pools. Yes, it certainly was lovely out there in the country!

The old castle, with its deep moat surrounding it, lay bathed in sunshine. Between the heavy walls and the edge of the moat there was a narrow strip of land covered by a whole forest of burdock plants. Their leaves were large and some of the stalks were so tall that a child could stand upright under them and imagine that he was in the middle of the wild and lonesome woods. Here a duck had built her nest.

While she sat waiting for the eggs to hatch, she felt a little sorry for herself because it was taking so long and hardly anybody came to visit her. The other ducks preferred swimming in the moat to sitting under a dock leaf and gossiping.

Finally the eggs began to crack. "Peep . . . Peep," they said one after another. The egg yolks had become alive and were sticking out their heads.

"Quack . . . Quack . . ." said their mother. "Look around you." And the ducklings did; they glanced at the green world around them, and that was what their mother wanted them to do, for green was good for their eyes.

"How big the world is!" piped the little ones, for they had much more space to move around in now than they had inside the egg.

"Do you think that this is the whole world?" quacked their mother. "The world is much larger than this. It stretches as far as the minister's wheat fields, though I have not been there. . . . Are you all here?"

The duck got up and turned around to look at her nest. "Oh, no, the biggest egg hasn't hatched yet; and I'm so tired of sitting here! I wonder how long it will take?" she wailed, and sat down again.

"What's new?" asked an old duck who had come visiting.

"One of the eggs is taking so long," complained the mother duck. "It won't crack. But take a look at the others. They are the sweetest little ducklings you have ever seen; and every one of them looks exactly like their father. That scoundrel hasn't come to visit me once."

"Let me look at the egg that won't hatch," demanded the old duck. "I am sure that it's a turkey egg! I was fooled that way once. You can't imagine what it's like. Turkeys are afraid of the water. I couldn't get them to go into it. I quacked and I nipped them, but nothing helped. Let me see that egg! . . . Yes, it's a turkey egg. Just let it lie there. You go and teach your young ones how to swim, that's my advice."

"I have sat on it so long that I guess I can sit a little longer, at least until they get the hay in," replied the mother duck.

"Suit yourself," said the older duck, and went on.

At last the big egg cracked too. "Peep . . . Peep," said the young one, and tumbled out. He was big and very ugly.

The mother duck looked at him. "He's awfully big for his age," she said. "He doesn't look like any of the others. I wonder if he could be a turkey? Well, we shall soon see. Into the water he will go, even if I have to kick him to make him do it."

The next day the weather was gloriously beautiful. The sun shone on the forest of burdock plants. The mother duck took her whole brood to the moat. "Quack . . . Quack . . ." she ordered.

One after another, the little ducklings plunged into the water. For a moment their heads disappeared, but then they popped up again and the little ones floated

like so many corks. Their legs knew what to do without
being told. All of the new brood swam very nicely, even
the ugly one.

"He is no turkey," mumbled the mother. "Look how
beautifully he uses his legs and how straight he holds
his neck. He is my own child and, when you look closely
at him, he's quite handsome. . . . Quack! Quack! Follow me and I'll take you to the henyard and introduce
you to everyone. But stay close to me, so that no one
steps on you, and look out for the cat."

They heard an awful noise when they arrived at the henyard. Two families of ducks had got into a fight over the head of an eel. Neither of them got it, for it was swiped by the cat.

"That is the way of the world," said the mother duck, and licked her bill. She would have liked to have the eel's head herself. "Walk nicely," she admonished them. "And remember to bow to the old duck over there. She has Spanish blood in her veins and is the most aristocratic fowl here. That is why she is so fat and has a red rag tied around one of her legs. That is the highest mark of distinction a duck can be given. It means so much that she will never be done away with; and all the fowl and the human beings know who she is. Quack! Quack! . . . Don't walk, waddle like well-brought-up ducklings. Keep your legs far apart, just as your mother and father have always done. Bow your heads and say, 'Quack!' " And that was what the little ducklings did.

Other ducks gathered about them and said loudly, "What do we want that gang here for? Aren't there enough of us already? Pooh! Look how ugly one of them is! He's the last straw!" And one of the ducks flew over and bit the ugly duckling on the neck.

"Leave him alone!" shouted the mother. "He hasn't done anyone any harm."

"He's big and he doesn't look like everybody else!" replied the duck who had bitten him. "And that's reason enough to beat him."

"Very good-looking children you have," remarked the duck with the red rag around one of her legs. "All of them are beautiful except one. He didn't turn out very well. I wish you could make him over again."

"That's not possible, Your Grace," answered the mother duck. "He may not be handsome, but he has a good character and swims as well as the others, if not a little better. Perhaps he will grow handsomer as he grows older and becomes a bit smaller. He was in the egg too long, and that is why he doesn't have the right

shape." She smoothed his neck for a moment and then added, "Besides, he's a drake; and it doesn't matter so much what he looks like. He is strong and I am sure he will be able to take care of himself."

"Well, the others are nice," said the old duck. "Make yourself at home, and if you should find an eel's head, you may bring it to me."

And they were "at home."

The poor little duckling, who had been the last to hatch and was so ugly, was bitten and pushed and made fun of both by the hens and by the other ducks. The turkey cock (who had been born with spurs on, and therefore thought he was an emperor) rustled his feathers as if he were a full-rigged ship under sail, and strutted up to the duckling. He gobbled so loudly at him that his own face got all red.

The poor little duckling did not know where to turn. How he grieved over his own ugliness, and how sad he was! The poor creature was mocked and laughed at by the whole henyard.

That was the first day; and each day that followed was worse than the one before. The poor duckling was chased and mistreated by everyone, even his own sisters and brothers, who quacked again and again, "If only the cat would get you, you ugly thing!"

Even his mother said, "I wish you were far away." The other ducks bit him and the hens pecked at him. The little girl who came to feed the fowls kicked him.

At last the duckling ran away. It flew over the tops of the bushes, frightening all the little birds so that they flew up into the air. "They, too, think I am ugly," thought the duckling, and closed his eyes—but he kept on running.

Finally he came to a great swamp where wild ducks lived; and here he stayed for the night, for he was too tired to go any farther.

In the morning he was discovered by the wild ducks. They looked at him and one of them asked, "What kind of bird are you?"

The ugly duckling bowed in all directions, for he was trying to be as polite as he knew how.

"You are ugly," said the wild ducks, "but that is no concern of ours, as long as you don't try to marry into our family."

The poor duckling wasn't thinking of marriage. All he wanted was to be allowed to swim among the reeds and drink a little water when he was thirsty.

He spent two days in the swamp; then two wild geese came—or rather, two wild ganders, for they were males. They had been hatched not long ago; therefore they were both frank and bold.

"Listen, comrade," they said. "You are so ugly that we like you. Do you want to migrate with us? Not far from here there is a marsh where some beautiful wild geese live. They are all lovely maidens, and you are so ugly that you may seek your fortune among them. Come along."

"Bang! Bang!" Two shots were heard and both the ganders fell down dead among the reeds, and the water turned red from their blood.

"Bang! Bang!" Again came the sound of shots, and a flock of wild geese flew up.

The whole swamp was surrounded by hunters; from every direction came the awful noise. Some of the hunters had hidden behind bushes or among the reeds but others, screened from sight by the leaves, sat on the long, low branches of the trees that stretched out over the swamp. The blue smoke from the guns lay like a fog over the water and among the trees. Dogs came splashing through the marsh, and they bent and broke the reeds.

The poor little duckling was terrified. He was about to tuck his head under his wing, in order to hide, when he saw a big dog peering at him through the reeds. The dog's tongue hung out of its mouth and its eyes glistened evilly. It bared its teeth. Splash! It turned away without touching the duckling.

"Oh, thank God!" he sighed. "I am so ugly that even the dog doesn't want to bite me."

The little duckling lay as still as he could while the shots whistled through the reeds. Not until the middle of the afternoon did the shooting stop; but the poor little duckling was still so frightened that he waited several hours longer before taking his head out from under his wing. Then he ran as quickly as he could out of the swamp. Across the fields and the meadows he went, but a wind had come up and he found it hard to make his way against it.

Toward evening he came upon a poor little hut. It was so wretchedly crooked that it looked as if it couldn't make up its mind which way to fall and that was why it was still standing. The wind was blowing so hard that the poor little duckling had to sit down in order not to be blown away. Suddenly he noticed that the door was off its hinges, making a crack; and he squeezed himself through it very carefully and was inside.

An old woman lived in the hut with her cat and her hen. The cat was called Sonny and could both arch his back and purr. Oh yes, it could also make sparks if you rubbed its fur the wrong way. The hen had very short legs and that was why she was called Cluck Lowlegs. But she was good at laying eggs, and the old woman loved her as if she were her own child.

In the morning the hen and the cat discovered the duckling. The cat meowed and the hen clucked.

"What is going on?" asked the old woman, and looked around. She couldn't see very well, and when she found the duckling she thought it was a fat, full-grown duck. "What a fine catch!" she exclaimed. "Now we shall have duck eggs, unless it's a drake. We'll give it a try."

So the duckling was allowed to stay for three weeks on probation, but he laid no eggs. The cat was the master of the house and the hen the mistress. They always referred to themselves as "we and the world," for they thought that they were half the world—and the better half at that. The duckling thought that he should be allowed to have a different opinion, but the hen did not agree.

"Can you lay eggs?" she demanded.

"No," answered the duckling.

"Then keep your mouth shut."

And the cat asked, "Can you arch your back? Can you purr? Can you make sparks?"

"No."

"Well, in that case, you have no right to have an opinion when sensible people are talking."

The duckling was sitting in a corner and was in a bad mood. Suddenly he recalled how lovely it could be outside in the fresh air when the sun shone: a great longing to be floating in the water came over the duckling, and he could not help talking about it.

"What is the matter with you?" asked the hen as soon as she had heard what he had to say. "You have nothing to do, that's why you get ideas like that. Lay eggs or purr, and such notions will disappear."

"You have no idea how delightful it is to float in the water, and to dive down to the bottom of a lake and get your head wet," said the duckling.

"Yes, that certainly does sound amusing," said the hen. "You must have gone mad. Ask the cat—he is the most intelligent being I know—ask him whether he likes to swim or dive down to the bottom of a lake. Don't take my word for anything. . . . Ask the old woman, who is the cleverest person in the world; ask her whether she likes to float and to get her head all wet."

"You don't understand me!" wailed the duckling.

"And if I don't understand you, who will? I hope you don't think that you are wiser than the cat or the old woman—not to mention myself. Don't give yourself airs! Thank your Creator for all He has done for you. Aren't you sitting in a warm room among intelligent people whom you could learn something from? While you, yourself, do nothing but say a lot of nonsense and aren't the least bit amusing! Believe me, that's the truth, and I am only telling it to you for your own good. That's how you recognize a true friend: it's someone who is willing to tell you the truth, no matter how unpleasant it is. Now get to work: lay some eggs, or learn to purr and arch your back."

"I think I'll go out into the wide world," replied the duckling.

"Go right ahead!" said the hen.

And the duckling left. He found a lake where he could float in the water and dive to the bottom. There were other ducks, but they ignored him because he was so ugly.

Autumn came and the leaves turned yellow and brown, then they fell from the trees. The wind caught them and made them dance. The clouds were heavy with hail and snow. A raven sat on a fence and screeched, "Ach! Ach!" because it was so cold. When just thinking of how cold it was is enough to make one shiver, what a terrible time the duckling must have had.

One evening just as the sun was setting gloriously, a flock of beautiful birds came out from among the rushes. Their feathers were so white that they glistened; and they had long, graceful necks. They were swans. They made a very loud cry, then they spread their powerful wings. They were flying south to a warmer climate, where the lakes were not frozen in the winter. Higher and higher they circled. The ugly duckling turned round and round in the water like a wheel and stretched his neck up toward the sky; he felt a strange longing. He screeched so piercingly that he frightened himself.

Oh, he would never forget those beautiful birds, those happy birds. When they were out of sight the duckling dove down under the water to the bottom of the lake; and when he came up again he was beside himself. He did not know the name of those birds or where they were going, and yet he felt that he loved them as he had never loved any other creatures. He did not envy them. It did not even occur to him to wish that he were so handsome himself. He would have been happy if the other ducks had let him stay in the henyard: that poor, ugly bird!

The weather grew colder and colder. The duckling had to swim round and round in the water, to keep just a little space for himself that wasn't frozen. Each night his hole became smaller and smaller. On all sides of him the ice creaked and groaned. The little duckling had to keep his feet constantly in motion so that the last bit of open water wouldn't become ice. At last he was too tired to swim any more. He sat still. The ice closed in around him and he was frozen fast.

Early the next morning a farmer saw him and with his clogs broke the ice to free the duckling. The man put the bird under his arm and took it home to his wife, who brought the duckling back to life.

The children wanted to play with him. But the duckling was afraid that they were going to hurt him, so he flapped his wings and flew right into the milk pail. From there he flew into a big bowl of butter and then into a barrel of flour. What a sight he was!

The farmer's wife yelled and chased him with a poker. The children laughed and almost fell on top of each other, trying to catch him; and how they screamed! Luckily for the duckling, the door was open. He got out of the house and found a hiding place beneath some bushes, in the newly fallen snow; and there he lay so still, as though there were hardly any life left in him.

It would be too horrible to tell of all the hardship and suffering the duckling experienced that long winter. It is enough to know that he did survive. When again the sun shone warmly and the larks began to sing, the duckling was lying among the reeds in the swamp. Spring had come!

He spread out his wings to fly. How strong and powerful they were! Before he knew it, he was far from the swamp and flying above a beautiful garden. The apple

trees were blooming and the lilac bushes stretched their
flower-covered branches over the water of a winding
canal. Everything was so beautiful: so fresh and green.
Out of a forest of rushes came three swans. They ruffled
their feathers and floated so lightly on the water. The

ugly duckling recognized the birds and felt again that strange sadness come over him.

"I shall fly over to them, those royal birds! And they can hack me to death because I, who am so ugly, dare to approach them! What difference does it make? It is better to be killed by them than to be bitten by the other ducks, and pecked by the hens, and kicked by the girl who tends the henyard; or to suffer through the winter."

And he lighted on the water and swam toward the magnificent swans. When they saw him they ruffled their feathers and started to swim in his direction. They were coming to meet him.

"Kill me," whispered the poor creature, and bent his head humbly while he waited for death. But what was that he saw in the water? It was his own reflection; and he was no longer an awkward, clumsy, gray bird, so ungainly and so ugly. He was a swan!

It does not matter that one has been born in the henyard as long as one has lain in a swan's egg.

He was thankful that he had known so much want, and gone through so much suffering, for it made him appreciate his present happiness and the loveliness of everything about him all the more. The swans made a circle around him and caressed him with their beaks.

Some children came out into the garden. They had brought bread with them to feed the swans. The youngest child shouted, "Look; there's a new one!" All the children joyfully clapped their hands, and they ran to tell their parents.

Cake and bread were cast on the water for the swans. Everyone agreed that the new swan was the most beautiful of them all. The older swans bowed toward him.

He felt so shy that he hid his head beneath his wing. He was too happy, but not proud, for a kind heart can never be proud. He thought of the time when he had been mocked and persecuted. And now everyone said that he was the most beautiful of the most beautiful birds. And the lilac bushes stretched their branches right down to the water for him. The sun shone so warm and brightly. He ruffled his feathers and raised his slender neck, while out of the joy in his heart, he thought, "Such happiness I did not dream of when I was the ugly duckling."

Hop aboard our magic carpet for an exciting trip to the mysterious land of ancient Persia. A boy named Aladdin is about to find a lamp. Not just an ordinary lamp, mind you—a special lamp, complete with a genie!

Aladdin and the Wonderful Lamp

Andrew Lang

THERE ONCE lived in Persia a boy called Aladdin. One day when he was playing in the street a stranger asked him his age, and if he was not the son of Mustapha the tailor.

"I am, sir," replied Aladdin, "but he died a long while ago."

At this the stranger fell on his neck and kissed him, saying, "I am your Uncle and I knew you from your likeness to my brother. Go to your Mother and tell her I am coming."

Aladdin ran home and told his Mother of his newly found Uncle.

"Indeed, child," she said, "your Father had a brother, but I always thought he was dead."

However, she prepared supper and bade Aladdin seek his Uncle, who came laden with wine and fruit. He told Aladdin's mother not to be surprised at not having seen him before, as for 40 years he had been out of the country.

Next day he led Aladdin a long way outside the city gates until they came to two mountains divided by a narrow valley. "We will go no farther," he said. "I will show you something wonderful. Gather up sticks while I kindle a fire."

When the fire was lit, he threw on it a powder he had with him, at the same time saying some strange words. The earth trembled a little and opened in front of them, disclosing a square flat stone with a brass ring in the middle to raise it by. Aladdin tried to run away, but his Uncle caught him and gave him a blow that knocked him down.

"What have I done, Uncle?" he said piteously.

Whereupon his Uncle said more kindly, "Fear nothing, but obey me. Beneath this stone lies a treasure that is to be yours, and no one else may touch it, so you must do exactly as I tell you."

At the word "treasure," Aladdin forgot his fears and grasped the ring as he was told. The stone came up quite easily, and some steps appeared.

"Go down," said his Uncle. "At the foot of those steps you will find an open door leading into three large halls. Tuck up your robe and go through them without touching anything, or you will die instantly. These halls lead into a garden of fine fruit trees. Walk on till you come to a niche in a terrace where stands a lighted lamp. Pour out the oil it contains and bring it to me." He drew a ring from his finger and gave it to Aladdin, bidding him prosper.

Aladdin found everything as his Uncle had said, gathered some fruit off the trees and, having got the lamp, arrived at the mouth of the cave.

His Uncle cried out in a great hurry, "Make haste

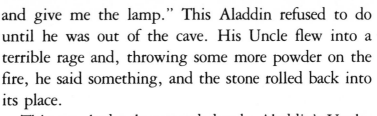

and give me the lamp." This Aladdin refused to do until he was out of the cave. His Uncle flew into a terrible rage and, throwing some more powder on the fire, he said something, and the stone rolled back into its place.

This man had only pretended to be Aladdin's Uncle. He was really a cunning magician who had read in his magic books of a wonderful lamp that would make him the most powerful man in the world. Though he alone knew where to find it, he could receive it only from the hand of Aladdin. Now, since he could not force the boy to give him the lamp, he returned to Africa, whence he had come.

Aladdin remained in the dark, crying and lamenting. At last he clasped his hands in prayer, and in so doing rubbed the ring, which the magician had forgotten to take from him.

Immediately a genie rose out of the earth, saying, "What wouldst thou with me? I am the slave of the ring and will obey thee in all things."

Aladdin fearlessly replied, "Deliver me from this place," whereupon the earth opened, and he found himself outside. When he came home he told his Mother what had passed, and showed her the lamp and the fruits he had gathered in the garden, which were in reality precious stones. He then asked for some food.

"Alas, child," she said, "I have nothing in the house, but I have spun a little cotton and will go and sell it."

Aladdin bade her keep her cotton, for he would sell the lamp instead. As it was very dirty she began to rub it, that it might fetch a higher price. Instantly a genie appeared and asked what she would have.

She fainted away, but Aladdin, snatching the lamp, said boldly, "Fetch me something to eat!"

The genie returned with a golden bowl, twelve gold plates containing rich meats, two gold cups, and a bottle of wine.

Aladdin's Mother, when she came to herself, said, "Whence comes this splendid feast?"

"Ask not, but eat," replied Aladdin.

So they sat at breakfast till it was dinner time, and Aladdin told his Mother about the lamp. When they had eaten all the genie had brought, Aladdin sold one of the gold plates, and so on till none were left. He then summoned the genie, who gave him another set of plates, and thus they lived for some years.

One day Aladdin heard an order from the Sultan proclaiming that everyone was to stay at home and close the shutters while the Princess, his daughter, went to and from the bath. Aladdin was seized by a desire to see her face, which was very difficult as she always went veiled. He hid himself behind the door of the bath and peeped through a chink.

The Princess lifted her veil as she went in, and looked so beautiful that Aladdin fell in love with her at first sight. He went home and told his Mother that he loved the Princess so deeply he could not live without her and meant to ask her father for her hand in marriage. His

Mother, on hearing this, burst out laughing, but Aladdin at last prevailed upon her to go before the Sultan and carry his request.

She fetched a napkin and laid in it the magic fruits from the enchanted garden, which sparkled and shone like the most beautiful jewels. The Grand Vizier and the lords of council had just gone into the palace hall as she arrived, so she went up to the foot of the throne and remained kneeling until the Sultan said to her, "Rise, good woman, and tell me what you want."

She hesitated, so the Sultan bade her speak freely, promising to forgive her beforehand for anything she might say. She then told him of her son's violent love for the Princess.

"I prayed him to forget her," she said, "but in vain; he threatened to do some desperate deed if I refused to go and ask Your Majesty for the hand of the princess. Now I pray you to forgive not me alone but my son Aladdin."

The Sultan asked her kindly what she had in the napkin, whereupon she unfolded the jewels and presented them.

He was thunderstruck, and turning to the Vizier, said, "What sayest thou? Ought I not to bestow the Princess on one who values her at such a price?"

The Vizier, who wanted her for his own son, begged the Sultan to withhold her for three months, in the course of which he hoped his son would contrive to make a richer present. The Sultan granted this and told Aladdin's Mother that, though he consented to the marriage, she must not appear before him again for three months.

Aladdin waited patiently for nearly three months, but then his Mother, going into the city to buy oil, found everyone rejoicing and asked what was going on.

"Do you not know," was the answer, "that the son of the Grand Vizier is to marry the Sultan's daughter tomorrow?"

Breathless, Aladdin's Mother ran and told him, and he sent her to remind the Sultan of his promise.

The Sultan said to her, "Good woman, your son must first send me 40 basins of gold brimful of jewels, carried by 40 black slaves and as many white ones, splendidly dressed. Tell him that I await his answer."

The Mother of Aladdin bowed low and went home, thinking all was lost. She gave Aladdin the message, adding, "He may wait long enough for your answer!"

"Not so long, Mother, as you think," her son replied. "I would do a great deal more than that for the Princess." He summoned the genie, and in a few moments the 80 slaves arrived and filled up the small house and garden.

Aladdin made them set out to the palace, followed by his Mother, who presented them to the Sultan.

He hesitated no longer, but said, "Good woman, return and tell your son that I wait for him with open arms."

She lost no time in telling Aladdin, bidding him make haste, but Aladdin first called the genie.

"I want a scented bath," he said, "richly embroidered clothes, a horse surpassing the Sultan's, and 14 slaves to attend me. Besides this I desire six slaves, beautifully dressed, to wait on my Mother; and lastly, 10,000 pieces of gold in 14 basins."

No sooner said than done. Aladdin mounted his horse and passed through the streets, the slaves strewing gold as they went.

When the Sultan saw him, he came down from his throne, embraced him, and led him into a hall where a feast was spread, intending to marry him to the Princess that very day. But Aladdin refused, saying, "I must build a palace fit for her," and took his leave.

Once home, he said to the genie, "Build me a palace of the finest marble, set with precious stones. In the middle you shall build me a large hall, each side having six windows. There must be stables and horses and grooms and 100 slaves. Go and see about it!"

The palace was finished the next day, and the genie carried Aladdin there and showed him all his orders faithfully carried out, even to the laying of a velvet carpet from his palace to the Sultan's. Aladdin's Mother then dressed herself carefully and walked to the palace with her slaves. The Sultan sent musicians with trumpets and cymbals to meet them, and the air resounded with music and cheers.

At night the Princess said good-bye to her father and set out on the carpet for Aladdin's palace, with his Mother at her side, and followed by the hundred slaves. After the wedding had taken place, Aladdin led her into the hall, where a feast was spread, and she supped with him, after which they danced till midnight.

They lived in peace and contentment for several years, but far away in Africa the magician remembered Aladdin and by his magic arts discovered that instead of perishing in the cave he had escaped and had married a Princess, with whom he was living in great honor and wealth. He knew that the poor tailor's son could have accomplished this only by means of the lamp, and he traveled day and night till he reached the capital of Persia. As he passed through the town he heard people talking everywhere about a marvelous palace.

"Forgive my ignorance," he said. "What is this palace you speak of?"

"Have you not heard of Prince Aladdin's palace," was the reply, "the greatest wonder of the world? I will direct you if you have a mind to see it."

When he saw the palace, the magician knew that it had been raised by the genie of the lamp. He bought a dozen copper lamps, put them into a basket, and went

to the palace, crying, "New lamps for old!" and followed by a jeering crowd.

The Princess, sitting in the hall of four and twenty windows, sent a slave to find out what the noise was about. The slave came back laughing, so the Princess scolded her.

"Madam," replied the slave, "who can help laughing to see an old fool offering to exchange fine new lamps for old ones?"

Another slave, hearing this, said, "There is an old one on the cornice there that he can have."

Now this was the magic lamp, which Aladdin had left there when he went hunting. The Princess, not knowing its value, laughingly bade the slave take it and make the exchange. She went and said to the magician, "Give me a new lamp for this."

He snatched it and bade the slave take her choice, amid the jeers of the crowd. Then he went out of the city gates to a lonely place, where he remained till nightfall, when he pulled out the lamp and rubbed it. The genie appeared and at the magician's command carried him, together with the palace and the Princess in it, to Africa.

Next morning the Sultan looked out of the window toward Aladdin's palace and rubbed his eyes, for it was gone. He sent 30 men on horseback to fetch Aladdin in chains. They met him riding home, bound him, and forced him to go with them on foot.

He was brought before the Sultan, and begged to know what he had done.

"False wretch," said the Sultan, "come hither," and showed him from the window the place where his palace had stood. Aladdin was so amazed that he could not say a word.

"Where are the palace and my daughter?" demanded the Sultan. "For the first I am not so deeply concerned, but my daughter I must have and you must find her or lose your head."

Aladdin begged for 40 days in which to find her, promising, if he failed, to return and suffer death at the Sultan's pleasure. His prayer was granted and he went forth sadly from the Sultan's presence. For three days he wandered about like a madman, asking everyone what had become of his palace, but they only laughed and pitied him.

He came to the banks of a river and knelt down to say his prayers before throwing himself in. In so doing he rubbed the magic ring he still wore. The genie he had seen in the cave appeared and asked his will.

"Save my life, genie," said Aladdin, "and bring my palace back."

"That is not in my power," said the genie. "I am only the slave of the ring; you must ask the slave of the lamp."

"Even so," said Aladdin, "but thou canst take me to

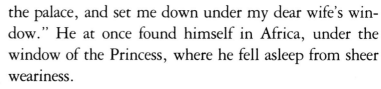

the palace, and set me down under my dear wife's window." He at once found himself in Africa, under the window of the Princess, where he fell asleep from sheer weariness.

Next morning she looked out and saw him. She called to him to come to her, and great was their joy at seeing each other again.

After he had kissed her Aladdin said, "I beg of you, Princess, before we speak of anything else, for your own sake and mine, tell me what has become of an old lamp I left on the cornice in the hall of four and twenty windows, when I went hunting."

"Alas," she said, "I am the innocent cause of our sorrows," and told him of the exchange of the lamp.

"Now I know," cried Aladdin, "that we have to thank the magician for this. Where is the lamp?"

"He carries it about with him," said the Princess. "I know, for he pulled it out of his robe to show me. He wishes me to break my faith with you and marry him, saying that you were beheaded by my father's command."

Aladdin comforted her and went into the nearest town, where he bought a certain powder. Then he returned to the Princess, who let him in by a little side door.

"Put on your most beautiful dress," he said to her, "and receive the magician with smiles, leading him to believe that you have forgotten me. Invite him to sup with you and say you wish to taste the wine of this country. He will go for some and I will tell you what to do while he is gone."

She listened carefully to Aladdin, and, when he left her, arrayed herself gaily for the first time since she left Persia. Then she received the magician, saying, "I have made up my mind that Aladdin is dead and that all my tears will not bring him back to me, so I am resolved to mourn no more and therefore invite you to sup with me. But I am tired of the wines of Persia and would gladly taste those of Africa."

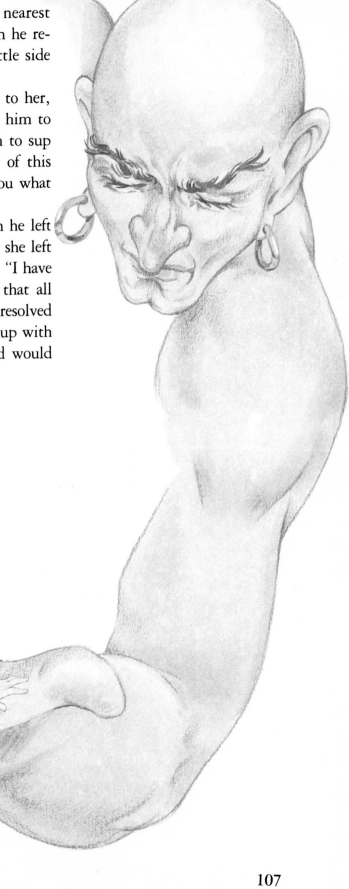

The magician flew to his cellar and the Princess put the powder Aladdin had given her in her cup. When he returned she asked him to drink her health in the wine of Africa, handing him her cup in exchange for his as a sign that she was reconciled to him. She set her cup to her lips while he drained his to the dregs and fell back in a deep sleep.

The Princess then opened the door to Aladdin, who took the lamp from the sleeping magician and summoned the genie. He bade him carry the magician outside and then transport the palace and all in it back to Persia. This was done, and the Princess felt only two slight shocks and could hardly believe she was at home again.

The Sultan, who was sitting in his closet mourning for his lost daughter, happened to look up and rubbed his eyes, for there stood the palace as before! He hastened there, and Aladdin received him in the hall of the four and twenty windows, with the Princess at his side.

After this Aladdin and his wife lived in peace. He succeeded the Sultan when he died, and reigned for many years, leaving behind him a long line of kings.

*Here is a delightful poem with a strong moral: Do
not form an opinion until you are sure you have the facts—
all of them!*

The Blind Men and the Elephant

John Godfrey Saxe

IT WAS SIX MEN of Indostan
   To learning much inclined,
Who went to see the elephant
   (Though all of them were blind),
That each by observation
   Might satisfy his mind.

The First approached the elephant,
   And, happening to fall
Against his broad and sturdy side,
   At once began to bawl:
"God bless me! but the elephant
   Is nothing but a wall!"

The Second, feeling of the tusk,
   Cried: "Ho! what have we here
So very round and smooth and sharp?
   To me 'tis mighty clear
This wonder of an elephant
   Is very like a spear!"

The Third approached the animal,
   And, happening to take
The squirming trunk within his hands,
   Thus boldly up and spake:
"I see," quoth he, "the elephant
   Is very like a snake!"

The Fourth reached out his eager hand,
    And felt about the knee:
"What most this wondrous beast is like
    Is mighty plain," quoth he;
" 'Tis clear enough the elephant
    Is very like a tree."

The Fifth, who chanced to touch the ear,
    Said: "E'en the blindest man
Can tell what this resembles most;
    Deny the fact who can,
This marvel of an elephant
    Is very like a fan!"

The Sixth no sooner had begun
   About the beast to grope,
Than, seizing on the swinging tail
   That fell within his scope,
"I see," quoth he, "the elephant
   Is very like a rope!"

And so these men of Indostan
   Disputed loud and long,
Each in his own opinion
   Exceeding stiff and strong,
Though each was partly in the right,
   And all were in the wrong!

So, oft in theologic wars
   The disputants, I ween,
Rail on in utter ignorance
   Of what each other mean,
And prate about an elephant
   Not one of them has seen!

One day after school Sam was doing some chores around his house when Sally called to him from next door.

"Who was Hercules, Sam?"

Sam noticed that Sally had a pen in one hand and some papers in the other.

"Is that your homework you're doing?" he asked.

"C'mon, Sam," Sally replied, "I don't want you to do my homework for me—just help me a little."

"OK," Sam answered, laughing. "I'll be right over."

A few minutes later Sally met Sam at the front door and invited him in. Sam was carrying a book with him. They sat in the living room and Sam opened the book.

"Hercules was the strongest man in the world, according to the ancient Greeks. Here's a story about Hercules. Not only was he strong, he was smart. Listen to this. . . ."

The Three Golden Apples

Adapted from A Wonder-Book for Girls and Boys, *by Nathaniel Hawthorne*

Hercules was a great hero, known both for his strength and kindness. In return for the King of Greece's promise not to harm his Stepfather, Hercules became the King's slave for 99 months. The King did not like Hercules and gave him twelve dangerous labors to do. For one of these labors, Hercules was told to bring back three golden apples from the garden of the Hesperides. It was a dangerous mission because any mortal who picked one of these apples would immediately die. Hercules traveled far to find the garden, and on his way some nymphs told him that he should ask for help from Atlas, the giant who holds up the sky.

THE GIANT WAS AS TALL as a mountain. So vast was he that the clouds rested about his middle, like a belt, and hung like a beard from his chin, and flitted before his huge eyes, so that he could not see Hercules. And, most wonderful of all, the giant held up his great hands and appeared to support the sky, which so far as Hercules could see, rested on his head!

Just then a breeze blew away the clouds from before the giant's face. Poor fellow! He had evidently stood there a long while. An ancient forest had been growing and decaying around his feet, and oak trees six or seven centuries old had sprung from the acorns and forced themselves between his toes. The giant now looked down from the far height of his great eyes, and seeing Hercules, roared out in a voice that resembled thunder, "Who are you, down at my feet there?"

"I am Hercules," thundered back the hero. "And I am seeking the garden of the Hesperides!"

"I am Atlas, the mightiest giant in the world! And I hold the sky upon my head."

"So I see," answered Hercules. "But can you show me the way to the garden of the Hesperides?"

"What do you want there?" asked the giant.

"I want three of the golden apples," shouted Hercules, "for my master the King."

"There is nobody but myself," quoth the giant, "that can go to the garden of the Hesperides and gather the apples. If it were not for this little business of holding up the sky, I would make half a dozen steps across the sea, and get them for you."

"Is the sky very heavy?" Hercules inquired.

"Why, not particularly so, at first," answered the giant, shrugging his shoulders. "But it gets to be after a thousand years!"

"And how long a time," asked the hero, "will it take you to get the golden apples?"

"Oh, that will be done in a few moments!" cried Atlas. "I will take ten or fifteen miles at a stride, and be at the garden and back again before your shoulders begin to ache."

"Well, then," answered Hercules, "I will climb the mountain behind you there, and relieve you of your burden." Without more words, the sky was shifted from the shoulders of Atlas and placed upon those of Hercules. Then Atlas stepped into the sea. His first stride covered ten miles. Hercules watched the giant as he went onward. It was a wonderful sight. But, as the gigantic shape faded entirely out of view, Hercules realized that the weight of the sky was already a little irksome to his shoulders.

"I really pity the poor giant," thought Hercules. "If it tires me so much in ten minutes, how it must have tired him in a thousand years."

I know not how long it was before, to his unspeakable joy, he beheld the huge shape of the giant. At his approach, Atlas held up his hand, in which Hercules could see three magnificent golden apples, as big as pumpkins, all hanging from one branch.

"I am glad to see you again," shouted Hercules. "So you have got the golden apples?"

"Certainly," answered Atlas, "and very fair apples they are. I took the finest that grew on the tree, I assure you."

"You have had a pleasant ramble and I heartily thank you for your trouble," said Hercules, "and now, as I have a long way to go, and am rather in haste, will you be kind enough to take the sky off my shoulders again? I would really appreciate the favor."

"Why, as to that," said the giant, "I have no fancy for burdening myself with the sky just now."

"What!" shouted Hercules. "Do you intend to make me bear this burden forever?"

"We will see about that one of these days," answered the giant. "At all events, you ought not to complain if you have to bear it the next hundred years, or perhaps the next thousand. I bore it a good while longer, in spite of the backache. Well, then, after a thousand years, if I happen to feel in the mood, we may possibly shift about again. You are certainly a very strong man, and can never have a better opportunity to prove it."

Hercules, being as clever as he was strong, said to the giant, "Just take the sky upon your head one instant, will you? I want to make a cushion of my lion's skin for the weight to rest on. It really chafes me, and will cause unnecessary inconvenience in so many centuries as I am to stand here."

"That's no more than fair, and I'll do it!" said the giant. "For just five minutes, then, I'll take back the sky. Only for five minutes, remember! I have no idea of spending another thousand years as I spent the last. Variety is the spice of life, I say!"

Ah, the thick-witted old rogue of a giant! He threw down the golden apples and received back the sky from the head and shoulders of Hercules onto his own, where it rightly belonged. And Hercules picked up the three golden apples and set out on his journey homeward.

And there stands the giant to this day, or, at any rate, there stands a mountain as tall as he, which bears his name. And when the thunder rumbles we may imagine it to be the voice of the Giant Atlas, bellowing after Hercules who tricked him.

*H*ere is another story from Greek myth. Like "The Three Golden Apples," this tale about the greedy King Midas was written by Nathaniel Hawthorne, one of the great American authors of the 19th century. Hawthorne wrote a number of stories for young people, collected in the volumes A Wonder-Book for Girls and Boys and Tanglewood Tales. Many of the stories in these books were based on Greek mythology. Hawthorne also wrote the ever popular novel The House of the Seven Gables.

The Golden Touch

Adapted from A Wonder-Book for Girls and Boys, *by Nathaniel Hawthorne*

ONCE UPON A TIME there lived a very rich man, and a king besides, whose name was Midas. He had a little daughter, whom nobody but myself ever heard of, and whose name I either never knew or have entirely forgotten. So, because I love odd names for little girls, I choose to call her Marygold.

This King Midas was fonder of gold than of anything else in the world. He valued his royal crown chiefly because it was composed of that precious metal. If he loved anything better, or half so well, it was the little maiden who played so merrily around her father's royal footstool.

But the more Midas loved his daughter, the more did he desire and seek for wealth. He thought—foolish man!—that the best thing he could possibly do for this dear child would be to bequeath her the most immense pile of yellow, glistening coin that had ever been heaped together since the world was made.

Thus, he gave all his thoughts and all his time to this one purpose. If ever he happened to gaze for an instant at the gold-tinted clouds of sunset, he wished that they were real gold, and that they could be squeezed safely into his strongbox. When little Marygold ran to meet him, with a bunch of buttercups and dandelions, he used to say, "Pooh, pooh, child! If these flowers were as golden as they look, they would be worth the trouble of plucking."

And yet, in his earlier days, before he was so entirely possessed of this desire for riches, King Midas had shown a great love for flowers. He had planted a garden, in which grew the biggest and loveliest and sweetest roses that any person ever saw or smelled. These roses were still growing in the garden, as large, as lovely, and as fragrant as when Midas used to pass whole hours in gazing at them and inhaling their perfume. But now, if he looked at them at all, it was only to calculate how much the garden would be worth if each of the countless rose petals were a thin plate of gold.

Midas called himself a happy man, but felt that he was not yet quite so happy as he might be. The very tiptop of enjoyment would never be reached unless the whole world were to become his treasure room, and be filled with gold.

Midas was enjoying himself in his treasure room one day when he noticed a shadow falling over the heaps of gold. Looking up suddenly, he beheld the figure of a stranger standing in the bright and narrow sunbeam! It was a young man, with a cheerful and ruddy face. Midas could not help fancying that the stranger's smile had a kind of golden radiance in it. Certainly, although his figure intercepted the sunshine, there was now a brighter gleam upon all the piled-up treasures than there was before.

Midas knew that he had carefully turned the key in the lock, and that no mortal strength could possibly break into his treasure room. He concluded that his visitor must be something more than mortal.

The stranger gazed about the room, and when his lustrous smile had glistened upon all the golden objects that were there, he turned again to Midas.

"You are a wealthy man, friend Midas," he observed. "I doubt whether any other four walls on earth contain so much gold as you have contrived to pile up in this treasure room."

"I have done pretty well, pretty well," answered Midas, in a discontented tone. "But, after all, it is but a trifle, when you consider that it has taken me my whole life to get it together. If one could live a thousand years, he might have time to grow really rich."

"What!" exclaimed the stranger. "Then you are not yet truly satisfied?"

Midas shook his head.

"And what would satisfy you?" asked the stranger. "Merely for the curiosity of the thing, would you tell me? I should be glad to know."

Midas paused and meditated. He had a feeling that

this stranger, with such a golden luster in his good-humored smile, had both the power and intention of gratifying his utmost wishes. At last a bright idea occurred to Midas. Raising his head, he looked the lustrous stranger in the face.

"I am weary of collecting my treasures with so much trouble," he said, "and beholding the heap so small, after I have done my best. I wish everything that I touch to be changed to gold."

The stranger's smile grew so very broad that it seemed to fill the room like an outburst of the sun.

"The Golden Touch," exclaimed he. "You certainly deserve credit, friend Midas, for striking upon so brilliant an idea. But are you quite sure this will finally satisfy you?"

"How could it fail?" said Midas.

"Be it as you wish, then," replied the stranger, waving his hand in farewell. "Tomorrow at sunrise you will find yourself gifted with the Golden Touch."

The figure of the stranger became exceedingly bright, and Midas had to close his eyes. When he opened them he was alone, surrounded by the piles of glistening treasure he had spent his life hoarding up.

Midas was wide awake the next morning when the earliest sunbeam shone through the window. It occurred to Midas that this bright yellow sunbeam made the white covers on his bed look like gold. Looking more closely, he was astonished to see that the linen cover had been changed into a fabric of the purest and brightest gold. The Golden Touch had come to him with the clear light of first sunbeam!

Midas jumped out of bed and ran about the room, grasping at everything that happened to be in his way. He seized one of the bedposts, and it became immediately a fluted golden pillar. He pulled open the window curtain, and the tassel grew heavy in his hand— a mass of gold. He took up a book from the table. At his first touch it turned to gold. But the pages had turned to thin golden sheets, and the writing in the book had become unreadable.

He hurriedly put on his clothes, and was enraptured to see himself in a magnificent suit of gold cloth. He drew out his handkerchief, which little Marygold had hemmed for him. That was likewise gold, with the dear child's neat and pretty stitches running all along the border in gold thread.

Somehow this last transformation did not quite please

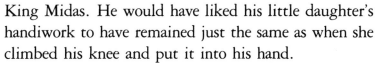

King Midas. He would have liked his little daughter's handiwork to have remained just the same as when she climbed his knee and put it into his hand.

Midas now took his spectacles from his pocket and put them on. To his disappointment, however, he discovered that he could not possibly see through them. The glass lenses had turned to shining yellow gold. It struck Midas as rather inconvenient that, with all his wealth, he could never again be rich enough to own a pair of usable eyeglasses.

"It is no great matter, nevertheless," said he to himself, very philosophically. "We cannot expect any great good without its being accompanied with some small inconvenience."

Wise King Midas then went downstairs and out to his garden, and everything he touched as he went turned to gold. In the garden he found a great number of roses in full bloom. Very delicious was their fragrance in the morning breeze.

But Midas knew a way to make them far more precious. He went from bush to bush and touched every one until each individual flower and bud had been turned to gold. Then he was summoned to breakfast, and hurried back to the palace.

Little Marygold had not yet made her appearance. Her father ordered her to be called and, seating himself at table, awaited the child's coming, in order to begin his own breakfast. Soon he heard her coming along the passageway, crying bitterly. This surprised him, because Marygold hardly shed a thimbleful of tears in a year. When Midas heard her sobs, he decided to raise her spirits with a surprise. So, leaning across the table, he touched his daughter's bowl—which was a China one, with pretty figures all around it—and turned it into gleaming gold.

Meanwhile, Marygold slowly opened the door, still sobbing as if her heart would break.

"How, now, my little lady!" cried Midas. "What is

the matter with you, this bright morning?"

Marygold held out one of the roses that King Midas had so recently changed to gold.

"As soon as I was dressed," she said, "I ran into the garden to gather some roses for you, because I know you like them. But all the beautiful, sweet-smelling roses are blighted and spoiled. They are grown quite yellow, and no longer have any fragrance."

"Pooh, my dear little girl—don't cry," said Midas, who was ashamed to confess that he himself had caused the roses to change. "Sit down and eat your breakfast. You will find it easy enough to change a golden rose like that for an ordinary one."

"I don't care for such roses as this," cried Marygold, tossing it away. "It has no smell, and the hard petals prick my nose."

Midas, meanwhile, had poured out a cup of coffee. Whatever metal the coffeepot had been when he picked it up, it was gold when he set it down. He lifted a spoonful of coffee to his lips, and, sipping it, was astonished to find that, the instant his lips touched the liquid, it turned to gold.

"Ha!" exclaimed Midas, rather aghast.

"What is the matter, father?" asked little Marygold, with the tears still standing in her eyes.

"Nothing, child, nothing," said Midas. "Eat your breakfast, before it gets quite cold."

Midas tried to eat a piece of toast, but as soon as he touched it, the toast turned into a slab of gold.

"I don't quite see," thought he to himself, "how I am to get any breakfast!"

So it went with every bit of food Midas tried to eat. As soon as he touched it, the food was changed to gold.

"Well, this is a problem," thought he, leaning back and watching Marygold, who was now enjoying her breakfast. "Such a costly breakfast before me, and nothing that can be eaten."

King Midas grabbed a hot potato and attempted to

cram it into his mouth and swallow it in a hurry. But he found his mouth full not of potato, but of solid metal, which so burned his tongue that he roared aloud. Jumping up from the table, he began to dance and stamp about the room, both with pain and fright.

"Father," cried little Marygold, "what is the matter? Have you burned your mouth?"

"Ah, dear child," groaned Midas, "I don't know what is to become of your poor father."

And, truly, the poorest laborer, sitting down to his crust of bread and cup of water, was far better off than King Midas, whose delicate food was really worth its weight in gold.

Midas again groaned aloud. Marygold could endure it no longer. She rose from her chair and, running to her father, threw her arms affectionately around him. He bent down and kissed her, but the moment his lips touched her forehead, her soft and tender little form grew hard and inflexible within her father's encircling arms. Oh, terrible misfortune! Little Marygold was a human child no longer, and now she was nothing more than a golden statue!

Midas began to wring his hands and bemoan himself, and he could neither bear to look at Marygold, nor yet look away from her. He would have been glad to become the poorest man in the wide world if the loss of all his wealth might bring back the faintest rose color to his dear child's face.

Midas suddenly beheld a stranger standing near the door. It was the same figure that had visited him the day before.

"Well, friend Midas," said the stranger, "how do you succeed with the Golden Touch."

Midas shook his head.

"I am miserable," said he.

"Miserable, indeed!" exclaimed the stranger. "And how happens that? Have I not faithfully kept my promise with you? Have you not everything that your heart desired?"

"Gold is not everything," answered Midas. "And I have lost all that my heart really cared for."

"Ah, so you have made a discovery since yesterday," observed the stranger. "Let us see then. Which of these two things do you think is really worth the most—the gift of the Golden Touch, or one cup of clear cold water?"

"Oh blessed water!" exclaimed Midas.

"The Golden Touch," continued the stranger, "or a crust of bread?"

"A piece of bread," answered Midas, "is worth all the gold on earth."

"The Golden Touch," asked the stranger, "or your own little Marygold?"

"Oh my child, my dear child!" cried poor Midas, wringing his hands.

"You are wiser than you were, King Midas," said the stranger. "Go then, and plunge into the river that

glides past the bottom of your garden. Take likewise a vase of the same water, and sprinkle it over any object that you may desire to change back again from the gold that it is now into its former substance. If you do this in earnestness and sincerity, it may possibly repair the mischief your greed has caused."

King Midas bowed low, and when he lifted his head, the lustrous stranger had vanished.

Midas lost no time in snatching up a great earthen pitcher—which instantly turned to gold—and hastening to the river's edge. On reaching the river he plunged in without waiting so much as to pull off his shoes.

"Poof! poof! poof!" snorted King Midas, as his head emerged out of the water. "Well, this is really a refreshing bath, and I think it must have quite washed away the Golden Touch. And now for the task of filling my pitcher!"

As he dipped the pitcher into the water, it gladdened his very heart to see it change from gold into the same good, honest earthen vessel it had been before he touched it. Seeing a violet growing on the bank of the river, Midas touched it with his finger, and was overjoyed to find that the delicate flower retained its purple hue instead of undergoing a yellow blight.

King Midas hastened back to the palace. The first thing he did was to sprinkle water over the golden figure of little Marygold.

No sooner did it fall on her than the rosy color came back to the dear child's cheek and she began to sneeze and sputter. How astonished she was to find herself dripping wet, and her father throwing water over her! For Marygold did not know that she had been a little golden statue, nor could she remember anything that had happened since the moment when she ran with outstretched arms to comfort her father.

Then Midas led little Marygold into the garden, where he sprinkled water over the rose bushes and all the roses recovered their beautiful bloom.

There were two things that, as long as he lived, reminded King Midas of the Golden Touch. One was that the sands of the river sparkled like gold. The other was that little Marygold's hair had now a golden tinge, which he had never observed in it before she had been changed by the effect of his kiss.

When King Midas had grown quite old, he liked to bounce Marygold's children on his knee and tell them this marvelous story. And then he would stroke their shiny curls and tell them that their hair, likewise, had a rich shade of gold, which they had inherited from their mother.

"And to tell you the truth, my precious little folks," he would say, "ever since that morning, I have hated the very sight of all other gold, save this!"

There are many good reasons why we should never tell a lie. This story is about a boy who learns he has a special reason to tell the truth. And rightly so, because he is a special kind of boy, the kind of boy you meet only in the wonderful world of books.

Pinocchio Learns to Tell the Truth

Retold by Eugene Ehrlich

IN A LITTLE TOWN IN ITALY, a long time ago, there lived an old man named Geppetto. For all his life Geppetto had worked as a carpenter. He had made fine furniture for rich men and women. He had built beautiful houses for many families. He once had even built a doll house for the young daughter of the King of Naples.

When Geppetto made that house, he built every bit of furniture for it. The tiny chairs and tables. A beautiful kitchen with all things needed for cooking. A living room with a couch and easy chairs. Bedrooms complete with beds and a dresser and closets.

Geppetto even made tiny dolls to live in the house. There was a mother doll, and there was a father doll. There was a little boy doll, and there was a little girl doll. All the dolls seemed so real to the Princess that she played with them for many years.

But that was long ago.

Now Geppetto was getting old. His hands were becoming stiff. His back often hurt when he worked for a time. And his eyes were not very strong. Geppetto knew that he would not be able to go on working for much longer. He would soon have to stop making furniture. He would have to stop building houses. He probably would never again have the chance to build a doll house for a princess.

Geppetto knew he would one day have to spend his time sitting in his little house, taking walks whenever the sun was out, and talking with his old friends while they sat together and watched young people go by.

None of this made Geppetto sad, for he knew that everyone must get old. He also knew that he had saved much of the money he had made during his life. He would never have to worry about having enough to eat or having a warm bed to sleep in. But Geppetto was not really happy.

What made Geppetto just a little bit sad was that he had never married, so he had no children to comfort him in his old age. He had no daughter to talk with. He had no son to teach his trade to or take walks with through the town. Geppetto knew he would eat alone for the rest of his days.

"If only I had a daughter or a son," Geppetto said to himself one day.

"Why not me?" said a voice.

"Eh, what's that? Who said that? Is there someone here in my workshop who is hiding from me?"

"I'm not hiding. I'm over here in your woodpile."

Geppetto got up from his chair and went to the woodpile. No one was there. Geppetto thought to himself, "I'm getting old. I'm beginning to hear voices even though no one is speaking."

"No, you're not. I'm speaking."

Sure enough, the voice seemed to be coming from the woodpile. Geppetto went back to the woodpile and began to take out the pieces one by one and put them down on the floor. When he got to the bottom, sure enough, he heard the voice again.

"That's better," said the voice. "You didn't know how uncomfortable it is to lie at the bottom of a woodpile. Take me out now."

Geppetto looked down at the last log in his woodpile. It looked just like all the other logs, but when Geppetto lifted it up, it spoke.

"Thank you, Geppetto."

"You're welcome, whoever you are."

"Whoever I am? If you'll put your carving knife to me, you'll soon find out that I'm a boy. And I'm going to be your boy."

At these words, Geppetto became very happy. "Is it possible," he thought, "that I finally will have a boy— a boy who will play happily, run errands for me, learn my trade, keep me company in my old age?"

Geppetto went to his workbench and prepared his carving knives and his sandpaper and his glue. When he had everything he needed, he put the log across his knees and set to work.

Geppetto worked the whole day and night through. He carved a head and a face and arms and legs and a sturdy body—all from the same log. And sure enough, when the first light of day appeared, Geppetto had finished his work. There was a boy, a beautiful boy with a head of black hair and blue eyes and a pointy nose, just like all the boys in the town.

And Geppetto called the boy Pinocchio.

Pinocchio was everything that Geppetto had wished for. He sang—as well as a wooden boy could—while Geppetto made breakfast. He danced—as well as a wooden boy could—while Geppetto made breakfast. He danced—as well as a wooden boy could—while Geppetto washed the dishes. He clapped his hands with happiness when Geppetto built a bed for Pinocchio to sleep in.

Every day from then on, Geppetto and Pinocchio would take walks together through the town. When Geppetto stopped to have a chat with his friends, Pinocchio would play with any children who happened to be around.

When Geppetto needed firewood, Pinocchio would go off to the woods and pick up what was needed. When Geppetto's shoes needed mending, Pinocchio would take them off to the cobbler. When Geppetto needed water for his cooking, Pinocchio would go to the town well to get it.

Pinocchio was eager to learn carpentry, and this made Geppetto happy. One by one Geppetto taught Pinocchio how to use all the tools a carpenter needs to build fine furniture, to build houses, to build doll houses. Pinocchio learned very quickly, and Geppetto knew that one day Pinocchio would be a first-class carpenter.

Soon Geppetto bought a fine hat for Pinocchio to wear—with a real feather in it. He bought Pinocchio a splendid jacket to wear. He even bought him shoes— one pair for everyday and a special pair for Sundays.

When Geppetto would go out for a walk with Pin-

occhio on a fine Sunday afternoon, all the townspeople
would see them.

"How nice your boy looks in his new clothes," they
would say.

"Geppetto, you should get yourself some new clothes
too," they would say.

"Who is that handsome young man with you?" they
would say.

The old man had never been happier in his life. He
had a good son.

Geppetto and Pinocchio took all their meals together,

and even though Pinocchio would go off to play with his friends after the evening meal, he would always be home before dark.

It happened that Pinocchio was off playing in the forest one day in midsummer, when the days were very long and the nights were very short. He had made friends with a rabbit, and on this day Pinocchio and the rabbit were playing tag together.

While Pinocchio was running away from the rabbit to keep from being tagged, Pinocchio tripped and fell. When he sat up, he found that he had fallen over a leather bag. He picked it up and looked inside.

"Oh my, there are three gold coins in this bag. I wonder whose they are."

The words were hardly out of his mouth when a beautiful Fairy Queen suddenly appeared before Pinocchio. She was dressed all in white and wore a golden crown on her head and carried a golden wand.

"What have you there, Pinocchio?"

"It's just a leather bag," he said thinking that if he could keep the coins for himself, he could buy enough candy with the coins to eat candy for the rest of his life.

"Is there anything in the bag?" said the Fairy Queen.

"No, it's quite empty."

At this, the Fairy Queen waved her wand in the air, and Pinocchio's nose began to itch.

"Why did you wave your wand?" said Pinocchio.

"Touch your nose and see," she said.

Pinocchio's nose had grown to twice its regular size! No wonder it itched! "Oh my," said Pinocchio. "How will I ever be able to go around town with such a nose? All the other boys will laugh at me. The birds will sit on my nose—there's enough room for twelve sparrows. And what if a woodpecker starts to work on the tip of my nose? Please, please help me."

"Are you sure there is nothing in the leather bag?" said the Fairy Queen.

"No. I told you before. There's nothing in the bag."

The Fairy Queen waved her wand in the air again, and again Pinocchio's nose began to itch even more.

"Don't tell me," said Pinocchio. "I don't have to touch my nose again to know what's happened. I can see that my nose has grown even bigger than before. Why have you done this to me? Now I can have 24 sparrows on my nose."

"I shall ask you just once more," said the Fairy Queen. "Is there anything in the leather bag?"

"Yes, oh yes!" said Pinocchio, whose nose was now so long that he thought it would break off. "There are three gold coins in the bag."

"Are you sure there are only three?" said the Fairy Queen.

"Oh yes. I am sure there are only three. Please do not make my nose grow any bigger. I can hardly reach the end of it. How will I ever be able to blow my nose?"

The Fairy Queen smiled at this and said, "Pinocchio, I have been watching you ever since you came to live with Geppetto. You have been a good boy up until today. But when I put that leather bag in front of you in order to make you fall and find it, I was testing you. I wanted to know whether you would tell a lie. And you did. You not only told one lie, you told two. That is not a good way to behave."

Pinocchio began to cry—as well as a wooden boy could cry. "I promise you, I will never tell a lie again. I promise."

As soon as Pinocchio finished talking, his nose began to itch again, and he could tell that his nose was beginning to return to its normal size. He reached up to touch it and found that his nose was once again just the size that Geppetto had carved.

"Oh, thank you, Fairy Queen," said Pinocchio. "Thank you for giving me back my real nose."

"Don't thank me for that," she said. "If you have truly learned that you must never lie again, then you have much more to thank me for than just your nose. Geppetto could have trimmed your nose every day, but only you can be truthful and reliable."

"Take your leather bag," said Pinocchio. "I'm sure you will want to have it back so you can teach other boys not to lie."

"No," said the Fairy Queen. "You take it home with you and give it to the good Geppetto. He will find the best use for the three gold coins."

With these words, the Fairy Queen vanished—as suddenly as she had appeared. Pinocchio was quite alone in the forest. He put the bag in the pocket of the jacket Geppetto had bought him and hurried home.

As soon as he closed the door behind him, Pinocchio gave the three gold coins to Geppetto.

"Where did you get these, Pinocchio?"

"In the forest. A Fairy Queen gave them to me."

"For telling that story, my boy, you'll have to go to bed without your dinner."

Pinocchio began to cry—as well as a wooden boy could cry—and told Geppetto the whole story. But Geppetto, who didn't believe in fairies, said, "I believe you think you are telling the truth, but just to be sure, you'll have to go to bed without your dinner anyway. Tomorrow I will ask all the townspeople whether they know anything about this gold. If no one knows whose gold it is, I will buy food for the poor families in our town."

"Well," Pinocchio said to himself later while he was getting into his bed, "Geppetto may have punished me even though I told the truth, but that's better than watching my nose get bigger. I'll never again tell a lie."

This poem was written by Ernest Lawrence Thayer in 1888, when major league baseball was still relatively young. The National League had been organized twelve years earlier, and the American League would not be established until 1900. But just about every American town of any size had a baseball team, professional or amateur, and just about every team had its hero. Here is the story of Mudville's finest, the mighty Casey.

Casey at the Bat

Ernest Lawrence Thayer

THE OUTLOOK wasn't brilliant for the Mudville nine that day;
The score stood four to two with but one inning more to play.
And then when Cooney died at first, and Barrows did the same,
A sickly silence fell upon the patrons of the game.

A straggling few got up to go in deep despair. The rest
Clung to that hope which springs eternal in the human breast;
They thought if only Casey could but get a whack at that—
We'd put up even money now with Casey at the bat.

But Flynn preceded Casey, as did also Jimmy Blake,
And the former was a lulu and the latter was a cake;
So upon that stricken multitude grim melancholy sat,
For there seemed but little chance of Casey's getting to the bat.

But Flynn let drive a single, to the wonderment of all,
And Blake, the much despisèd, tore the cover off the ball;
And when the dust had lifted, and the men saw what had occurred,
There was Jimmy safe at second and Flynn a-hugging third.

Then from five thousand throats and more there rose a lusty yell;
It rumbled through the valley, it rattled in the dell;
It knocked upon the mountain and recoiled upon the flat,
For Casey, mighty Casey, was advancing to the bat.

There was ease in Casey's manner as he stepped into his place;
There was pride in Casey's bearing and a smile on Casey's face.
And when, responding to the cheers, he lightly doffed his hat,
No stranger in the crowd could doubt 'twas Casey at the bat.

Ten thousand eyes were on him as he rubbed his hands with dirt;
Five thousand tongues applauded when he wiped them on his shirt.
Then while the writhing pitcher ground the ball into his hip,
Defiance gleamed in Casey's eye, a sneer curled Casey's lip.

And now the leather-covered sphere came hurtling through the air,
And Casey stood a-watching it in haughty grandeur there.
Close by the sturdy batsman the ball unheeded sped—
"That ain't my style," said Casey. "Strike one," the umpire said.

From the benches, black with people, there went up a muffled roar,
Like the beating of the storm waves on a stern and distant shore.
"Kill him! Kill the umpire!" shouted someone on the stand;
And it's likely they'd have killed him had not Casey raised his hand.

With a smile of Christian charity great Casey's visage shone;
He stilled the rising tumult; he bade the game go on;
He signaled to the pitcher, and once more the spheroid flew;
But Casey still ignored it, and the umpire said, "Strike two."

"Fraud!" cried the maddened thousands, and echo answered, "Fraud!"
But one scornful look from Casey and the audience was awed.
They saw his face grow stern and cold, they saw his muscles strain,
And they knew that Casey wouldn't let that ball go by again.

The sneer is gone from Casey's lip, his teeth are clenched in hate;
He pounds with cruel violence his bat upon the plate.
And now the pitcher holds the ball, and now he lets it go,
And now the air is shattered by the force of Casey's blow.

Oh, somewhere in this favored land the sun is shining bright;
The band is playing somewhere, and somewhere hearts are light,
And somewhere men are laughing, and somewhere children shout;
But there is no joy in Mudville—mighty Casey has struck out.

Here is an episode from the book Through the Looking Glass *by Lewis Carroll. In the book, a sequel to Carroll's masterpiece,* Alice's Adventures in Wonderland, *Alice steps through a mirror into a curious and fantastic world. In her travels she gets involved in a giant chess game. Along the way she meets a number of interesting characters, including this well-known figure of nursery rhyme fame.*

Alice Meets Humpty Dumpty

Lewis Carroll

THE EGG GOT LARGER and larger, and more and more human. When she had come within a few yards of it, she saw that it had eyes and a nose and a mouth. And when she had come close to it, she saw clearly that it was Humpty Dumpty himself. "It can't be anybody else!" she said to herself. "I'm as certain of it as if his name were written all over his face."

Humpty Dumpty was sitting with his legs crossed, like a Turk, on the top of a high wall—such a narrow one that Alice quite wondered how he could keep his balance—and, as his eyes were steadily fixed in the opposite direction, and he didn't take the least notice of her, she thought he must be a stuffed figure after all.

"And how exactly like an egg he is!" she said aloud, standing with

her hands ready to catch him, for she was every moment expecting him to fall.

"It's *very* provoking," Humpty Dumpty said after a long silence, looking away from Alice as he spoke, "to be called an egg—*very!*"

"I said you *looked* like an egg, Sir," Alice gently explained. "And some eggs are very pretty, you know," she added, hoping to turn her remark into a sort of compliment.

"Some people," said Humpty Dumpty, looking away from her as usual, "have no more sense than a baby!"

Alice didn't know what to say to this. It wasn't at all like conversation, she thought, as he never said anything to *her.* In fact, his last remark was evidently addressed to a tree—so she stood and softly repeated to herself:

> *Humpty Dumpty sat on a wall:*
> *Humpty Dumpty had a great fall.*
> *All the King's horses and all the King's men*
> *Couldn't put Humpty Dumpty in his place again.*

"That last line is much too long for the poetry," she added, almost out loud, forgetting that Humpty Dumpty would hear her.

"Don't stand chattering to yourself like that," Humpty Dumpty said, looking at her for the first time, "but tell me your name and your business."

"My *name* is Alice, but —"

"It's a stupid name enough!" Humpty Dumpty interrupted impatiently. "What does it mean?"

"Must a name mean something?" Alice asked.

"Of course it must," Humpty Dumpty said with a short laugh. "*My* name means the shape I am—and a good handsome shape it is, too. With a name like yours, you might be any shape, almost."

"Why do you sit out here all alone?" said Alice, not wishing to begin an argument.

"Why, because there's nobody with me!" cried Humpty Dumpty. "Did you think I didn't know the

answer to *that*? Ask another."

"Don't you think you'd be safer down on the ground?" Alice went on, not with any idea of making another riddle, but simply in her good-natured anxiety for the queer creature. "That wall is so very narrow!"

"What tremendously easy riddles you ask!" Humpty Dumpty growled out. "Of course I don't think so! Why, if ever I *did* fall off—which there's no chance of—but *if* I did—" Here he pursed up his lips and looked so solemn and grand that Alice could hardly help laughing. "*If* I did fall," he went on, "the King has promised me—ah, you may turn pale, if you like! The King has promised me, with his very own mouth, to—"

"To send all his horses and all his men," Alice interrupted, rather unwisely.

"Now I declare that's too bad!" Humpty Dumpty cried, breaking into a sudden passion. "You've been listening at doors, and behind trees, and down chimneys, or you couldn't have known it!"

"I haven't, indeed!" Alice said very gently. "It's in a book."

"Ah, well! They may write such things in a *book*," Humpty Dumpty said in a calmer tone. "That's what you call a History of England, that is. Now, take a good look at me! I'm one that has spoken to a King, *I* am. Mayhap you'll never see such another, and to show you I'm not proud, you may shake hands with me!" And he grinned almost from ear to ear, as he leant forward (and as nearly as possible fell off the wall in doing so) and offered Alice his hand.

She watched him a little anxiously as she took it. "If he smiled much more, the ends of his mouth might meet behind," she thought, "and then I don't know what would happen to his head! I'm afraid it would come off!"

"Yes, all of his horses and all his men," Humpty Dumpty went on. "They'd pick me up again in a minute, they would! However, this conversation is going on a little too fast. Let's go back to the last remark but one."

"I'm afraid I can't quite remember it," Alice said very politely.

"In that case we start fresh," said Humpty Dumpty, "and it's my turn to choose a subject." (He talks about it just as if it was a game! thought Alice.) "So here's a question for you. How old did you say you were?"

Alice made a short calculation, and said, "Seven years and six months."

"Wrong!" Humpty Dumpty exclaimed triumphantly. "You never said a word like it!"

"I thought you meant 'How old are you?'" Alice explained.

"If I'd meant that, I'd have said it," said he.

Alice didn't want to begin another argument, so she said nothing.

"Seven years and six months!" Humpty Dumpty repeated thoughtfully. "An uncomfortable sort of age. Now if you'd asked *my* advice, I'd have said 'Leave off at seven'—but it's too late now."

"I never ask advice about growing," Alice said indignantly.

"Too proud?" the other inquired.

Alice felt even more indignant at this suggestion. "I mean," she said, "that one can't help growing older."

"*One* can't, perhaps," said Humpty Dumpty, "but *two* can. With proper assistance, you might have left off at seven."

"What a beautiful belt you've got on!" Alice suddenly remarked. (They had had quite enough of the subject of age, she thought, and if they really were to take turns in choosing subjects, it was her turn now.) "At least," she corrected herself on second thoughts, "a beautiful cravat, I should have said—no, a belt, I mean—I beg your pardon!" she added in dismay, for Humpty Dumpty looked thoroughly offended, and she began to wish she hadn't chosen that subject. "If only I knew," she thought to herself, "which was his neck and which was his waist!"

Evidently Humpty Dumpty was very angry, though he said nothing for a minute or two. When he *did* speak again, it was in a deep growl.

"It is a most provoking thing," he said at last, "when a person doesn't know a cravat from a belt!"

"I know it's very ignorant of me," Alice said, in so humble a tone that Humpty Dumpty relented.

"It's a cravat, child, and a beautiful one, as you say. It's a present from the White King and Queen!"

"Is it really?" said Alice, quite pleased to find that she *had* chosen a good subject, after all.

"They gave it me," Humpty Dumpty continued thoughtfully, as he crossed one knee over the other and clasped his hands round it, "they gave it me—for an un-birthday present."

"I beg your pardon?" Alice said with a puzzled air.

"I'm not offended," said Humpty Dumpty.

"I mean, what *is* an un-birthday present?"

"A present given when it isn't your birthday, of course," Humpty Dumpty answered.

Alice considered a little. "I like birthday presents best," she said at last.

"You don't know what you're talking about!" cried Humpty Dumpty. "How many days are there in a year?"

"Three hundred and sixty-five," said Alice.

"And how many birthdays have you?"

"One."

"And if you take one from three hundred and sixty-five, what remains?"

"Three hundred and sixty-four, of course."

Humpty Dumpty looked doubtful. "I'd rather see that done on paper," he said.

Alice couldn't help smiling as she took out her memorandum book, and worked the sum for him:

$$365$$
$$-1$$
$$364$$

Humpty Dumpty took the book and looked at it carefully. "That seems to be done right," he began.

"You're holding it upside down!" Alice interrupted.

"To be sure I was!" Humpty Dumpty said gaily, as she turned it round for him. "I thought it looked a little queer. As I was saying, that *seems* to be done right—though I haven't time to look it over thoroughly just now—and that shows that there are three hundred and sixty-four days when you might get un-birthday presents. And only *one* for birthday presents, you know!"

This is a story from the Ashanti tribe of western Africa, in the country that now is Ghana. In some ways this tale is much like the fables of Aesop. For example, the animals talk with each other, as in "The Ant and the Grasshopper." In fact, the monkey in this story is very much like Aesop's very lazy grasshopper.

The King's Drum

Harold Courlander

THE KING OF THE FOREST once called a meeting of all his subjects. His messengers went out to distant villages, and when the animals heard the King's command, they put on their best clothes and began their trip. But many weeks passed before they arrived.

When they had all gathered before his house, the King said to them: "When a meeting is called, many days pass before we are gathered. This is not good. What if we are in danger? What if the enemy is coming? We must find a way to gather quickly."

Anansi the spider was the King's counselor. He said, "What is needed is a drum. When the royal drum is beaten, it will be heard everywhere. Everyone will come quickly."

The animals applauded Anansi's suggestion. It was agreed that there should be a drum. The King ordered that a drum should be made. The animals were organized into work squads. Each squad was to take its turn at the making of the drum. First, one squad went out and cut a tree. Another squad went out to trim the tree. Another squad took adzes and cut the tree into the shape of a drum. The drum was hollowed. After that, carvers were set to work to decorate the drum. Only the monkey did not do any work. While the others labored, the monkey found a shady place and slept, or he went off looking for berries. When they came back to the village, the animals sang:

"Life is labor,
 We are tired,
 We are hot,
 It is for the King we labor."

The monkey also sang:
"Life is labor,
  I am tired,
  I am hot,
  It is for the King I labor."
But Anansi saw that the monkey shirked and rested while the others labored. He said nothing.

A time came when the drum was finished. The King announced: "Let the drum be brought in. There will be a ceremony. The drum will be initiated. After that, the assembly will be ended. When the people are wanted again, the royal drum will be sounded."

Anansi said, "Yes, the drum shall be brought in. There is only one problem remaining. Who shall carry the drum?"

The drum was very large. It was heavy. The distance was great. No one wanted to carry it.

The leopard said, "Let the lion receive the honor."

The lion said, "No, it is the antelope who should carry it."

The antelope declared, "No, it is more fitting for the elephant to do it."

Each animal suggested that another should have the honor.

Anansi said, "It appears that each person wants someone else to do the carrying. Therefore, I suggest that the person to carry the drum is he who is most lazy."

The King said, "Yes, that is the way to do it."

The animals considered the question. They looked at each other. They tried to think who was the laziest. First, one looked at the monkey, then another looked at the monkey. The monkey looked here, looked there. Everywhere he looked, he saw people looking at him.

He went to the middle of the crowd and said: "I wish to make a statement. I refuse to carry the drum. Never, never will I carry the drum. That is all I have to say."

All the animals laughed. The antelope said, "Why

are you here? No one mentioned your name."

The porcupine said, "Why do you speak? No one asked you to carry the drum."

The crowd called out, "Yes, no one said even a word to him."

Once more the monkey said: "I want it to be made clear. I will not carry the drum. These are my words."

Again the animals laughed.

Anansi said to the King:

"No one mentioned the monkey's name. People were thinking to themselves, 'Who is the laziest?' They could not make up their minds. But the monkey was sure. He came forward. He said, 'I want it made clear that I will never carry the drum.' Thus he confessed that he is the laziest. With his own mouth he has said it."

The animals answered, "It is true, the monkey is the laziest of all!"

And so when at last the great drum was brought from the forest to the King's house, it was the monkey who carried it.

One day late in October, Sam awoke to hear a slow, rhythmic, hammering type of sound coming from next door. He rose and got dressed and went outside to investigate. Next door he found Sally helping her father, who was splitting wood with an axe.

"I'm getting this wood ready for our new wood-burning stove," Sally's father told Sam.

"You look like Paul Bunyan," Sally said.

"I don't feel like him (puff puff)," Sally's father replied.

"What do you feel like?"

"I feel like taking a break."

While they were resting and drinking some hot chocolate, Sam and Sally inspired her Dad by reading him this story about Paul Bunyan.

Paul's Great Flapjack Griddle

From Paul Bunyan and His Great Blue Ox
Retold by Wallace Wadsworth

WHEN PAUL BUNYAN ARRIVED in the Dakotas, he was very much pleased over the prospects there of being able to set up a new logging record. The timberlands of those states were ideal for his work, the easy conditions being quite different from the harsh ones he had known in Maine and the other eastern states. In the first place, most of the land was so level that it was very easy to get the logs to the streams, and the trails

were already so straight that there was but little work for Babe to do in straightening them. In fact, this new location was just about all that could be desired for logging on a tremendous scale, and Paul set to work with great enthusiasm.

Paul had been accompanied westward by most of the men who had been with him in Maine. There were the Seven Axmen, the Little Chore Boy, and the faithful Ole, of course. Then, in addition, there were such famous loggers as Chris Crosshaul, Hard-jaw Murphy, Windy Night, Red-nose Jack and Blue-nose Mack, Shot Gunderson, Handy Hank, Brimstone Bill, and a whole host of others, mighty workers every one of them, and all as proud as pouter pigeons to be working for such a boss as Paul Bunyan.

Both Babe and Willie, the Big and Little Blue Oxen, came along, too, following close on their master's heels all the way and carrying on their backs all the tools, supplies, and other property that was to be used in the new camp. Some historians think that Paul also moved all of his camp buildings to the Dakotas, but that was probably done on one of his later moves, as the biggest building from his Maine camp would hardly have been big enough even for a tool house in his Red River Camp, after it got to going full blast.

Paul left his old camp in Maine very early in the morning, and so anxious was he to get located in his new camp that he hurried along at quite a fast pace, so that he arrived on the banks of what was afterwards called the Red River along about sunset of that afternoon. Most of his men kept up with him pretty well, but some of the stragglers didn't arrive until along some time the next morning.

Paul saw at once that he would be able to work very fast in clearing off this level land. "These pines must be a new variety," he said to the Big Swede. "I have never seen any quite like them before. Do you notice how none of them stand up straight, but all lean the

same way? I think I'll give them the name of 'Leaning Pines,' and notify the tree experts back East so they can write about them in books." Indeed, there was something very peculiar about the big trees that covered the land so thickly, for they all leaned at just exactly the same angle toward the south.

Ole, however, shook his head over what Paul had said. "Ay tank they bane ordinary White Pines," he disagreed. "Ay tank Hugags make 'em lean that way." It so happened that this time Ole was more right than Paul, for the leaning trees were not a new species at all. Their strange peculiarity had been caused, as the Big Swede suspected, by the Hugag, a frightful looking but entirely harmless animal which was then to be found in great numbers in the Dakota woods.

The Hugag was quite large, with a body like a buffalo, and often weighed as much as two tons. Its head and neck were absolutely hairless, its wrinkled ears flopped downward, its bushy tail waggled constantly, and it had long muscular lips which prevented it from feeding on grass or other low-growing herbage, but which were of the greatest use—like the trunk of an elephant—in stripping from trees the bark and twigs which were its usual food. Its greatest oddity, though, was its legs. They were long and stiff and perfectly straight, being entirely without joints in them, and since they therefore could not be bent the Hugag could never

lie down as other animals do. It lived its whole life, waking and sleeping, upon its feet. Occasionally one would by some chance fall or be thrown to the ground, and as it could not bend its legs to get to its feet again, it was then perfectly helpless and soon died of fright or starvation.

Its strange manner of sleeping was the cause of the leaning pines. When it wanted to take a nap, it would face the west and lean its left side against the trunk of a pine tree, brace its hind legs firmly but never ceasing to mark time with its splay-footed front ones, hang down its head and close its eyes, and in this manner it would rest comfortably. Countless Hugags had followed these exact habits through many centuries, and the pressure of their weight against the trees of the Dakota woods had after many years caused all the pines to lean toward the south in the manner which had at first deceived Paul.

The most successful hunters of this queer animal followed the custom of cutting partly through the bases of trees until they were almost ready to fall, so that when the Hugag leaned against one both the tree and animal would come down. As it could not then get to its feet again, it was easily captured or killed. Since the Hugag has almost entirely disappeared, this method of hunting has been abandoned and forgotten, as it has never proven successful with any other animal.

The uniform slant of the trees was a great aid in cutting them, for they all fell in exactly the same direction without any guidance on the part of the cutters. Paul was therefore able to use his great three-mile saw to the best advantage. When its blade passed through the forest, it ate its way through the thousands of trunks in its path like a mowing machine in a hay field, and left the trees lying evenly side by side in windrows on the ground, ready to be cut into logs and snaked away.

Paul was so strong that he did not have to have much help with the big saw, and he usually put the Little

Chore Boy on the other end to balance it down. He didn't care whether the Little Chore Boy did much saw work with the other end or not, and he never said anything when the youngster would hang onto the saw handle and ride back and forth as the blade cut through the trees, but he did occasionally get a little angry when the lad thoughtlessly allowed his feet to drag on the ground.

After the full crew got to working in the Dakota woods, the trees were cut down so fast that it was not very long before the poor Hugags could no longer find places to lean, and as a result they soon began perishing for lack of sleep. Nearly all of them died during the winter that Paul had his big camp on the Red River, and it is only very rarely that a stray one has been seen since that time.

It was on the banks of the Red River of the North that Paul had set up his camp, and there he assembled one of the greatest logging crews that has ever existed. So many men did he have in camp that one of his bunkhouses had a hundred and thirty-seven tiers of bunks, and the men used to go to bed with balloons and come down in the morning with parachutes. It was a pretty sight to see them early of a morning pouring out of their bunks and floating down in great clouds just about the time that the cooks were getting breakfast well under way.

No alarm clocks were needed in Paul's camp. He knew lumberjacks pretty well, Paul did, and so he just had a big pipe stretched from the cook shanty to the bunkhouses and a blower fixed in it. In the morning, when the cooks had their fires going, the victuals beginning to cook and the coffee simmering, the blower fan was turned on and the smell of breakfast blown right into the bunkhouses. Then, if a jack didn't grab his parachute and jump out of his bunk right away the camp doctor was sent to look him over, for every one knew that he must be sick.

Paul found that feeding his many men was a good deal of a job, and especially did he find it hard to give them all the flapjacks they wanted, for they all seemed to have developed an extraordinary craving for this favorite delicacy. Since all of his men were so fond of flapjacks, he had to figure out some way to give them all they wanted, for he liked to keep his helpers satisfied.

The special flapjack stove which he had brought with him from Maine had disappeared in a very strange manner shortly after his arrival in the Dakotas. The queer passion for hot cakes which constantly stirred Willie, the Little Blue Ox, had grown rather than abated, and one morning he had stuck his head into the kitchen and eaten the day's supply at one gulp. He topped off this tidbit by swallowing the redhot flapjack stove as dessert, and as a result he developed a very painful case of stomach ache from which he soon died. Just what Paul did with his body is not certain, though the story goes that he sold the carcass that year (it was about 1857 when Willie died, it is said) to various packing companies in Chicago. These meat packers made a very good thing out of the remains of poor Willie, working him up and selling him for high prices.

Not all of their stock has been disposed of yet, so much of him was there, and thousands of people in this day and age are familiar with "canned Willie." It is rumored that most of him that was still on hand when the Great War broke out was sold to the government to feed the soldiers and sailors, and some day there may be an investigation to find out if this is true or not.

Paul Bunyan puzzled over the problem of getting enough flapjacks for his men, and finally he ordered Big Ole to make him a huge griddle. So big was this griddle that the cookees greased it with telephone poles on the ends of which were tied great bunches of gunny sacks for swabs. As Paul kept on hiring more men all the time, however, it was not very long before it became far too small, and he had his problem to settle all over again.

Some one at last told him where he could get a much bigger griddle to take the place of the one that was now outgrown, but it was so large that he couldn't at first figure out how to get it to camp. Luckily it was perfectly round in shape, and though it was so thick when it was stood on edge that it made a track as wide as a wagon

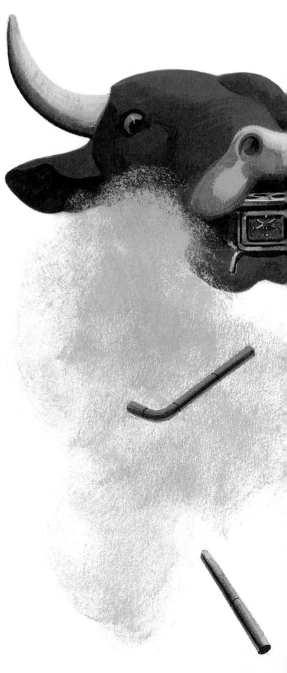

road and was terribly hard to lift, Paul soon thought out a way to get it to the place where he wanted it.

Being so hard pressed by the need of more flapjacks in camp, he had started working the inventive side of his brain again, and it was at this time that he invented the electromagnet. He and Ole made two enormous big ones so strong that when they were tested out for the first time they pulled all the axes and saws and other tools out of the hands of the men in the woods within five miles of the camp. Seeing the trouble they had caused, Paul shut off the magnets at once, but it was worse than jigsaw puzzle sorting out all the things that had been pulled into camp. He was quite pleased, how-ever, with such a demonstration by the magnets, for he knew that they were just the things to help him get the big griddle to where he wanted it.

Shortly before this he had bought a team of mules, Jerry and Jinny, intending to use them occasionally while he gave Babe a rest. This mule team could travel so fast, after they had had their regular feed of ten bush-els of wheat apiece, that no one else could hold them in, and so Paul always had to drive them himself. He used them hitched to a big flat-bottomed wagon without wheels.

So now he harnessed his mules up, fixed his new magnets in the back of the wagon, and drove off to where the griddle was. He swung the magnets around until their strength drew the griddle right up on its edge, and then he drove off lippity-cut toward the camp. The pull of the magnets got the griddle going around so fast and following him at such a great rate of speed that he hardly knew how to stop it, for the faster the mules went, just that much faster did the griddle roll along behind trying to catch up. It was clearly impos-sible for him to run away from it.

When he at last passed over the spot where he wanted it, he just dropped the magnets out of the wagon and pulled up to one side to watch what would happen. It rolled around and around, like a big pie pan circling about on the floor as it loses its speed after some one spins it, getting nearer and nearer to where the magnets lay. It kept rolling weaker and weaker, until finally it twisted around a couple of times more just at the place where he wanted it, and gouged out a big hole in the ground as it turned. Then it settled down, as nice as you please, right flat over the hole it had dug, and there it was at last, all ready for use and with a place for the fire underneath.

Paul then built a high fence around the griddle, and right beside it he put a couple of big buildings to hold his pancake flour. So perfectly did he have these buildings arranged that others just like them are used today as elevators for storing grain. He also invented a machine for mixing up the hot cake batter, and had Ole make eight or ten of them, which were placed in position by the griddle. These machines of Paul's are also copied today, and any one may see many small models of them being used by paving contractors for mixing concrete.

"There now," said Paul to Sourdough Sam, the head baker of the camp, who also had charge of all the flapjack making, "there is a griddle to be proud of—a griddle which it should be a pleasure to work with. Everything is nice and handy, there is plenty of room to insure the best of results, and from now on you should find the subject of flapjacks as interesting as that of your sourdough bread."

Sam was doubtful at first, for he had had several disastrous experiments with flapjacks in the past—once having his mixing vat burst and flood the landscape for miles around with thin and sticky flapjack batter—and he was not at all optimistic about making hot cakes on the tremendous scale which Paul had just made provision for. However, after he began to get used to the new arrangements, he began also to get interested in the intricacies of flapjack making. It was not long, therefore, until he was turning out his giant hot cakes with all

the artistry which he had hitherto reserved exclusively for his first love, sourdough bread. From that time on his flapjacks were so wonderful that men still talk about them, and no other griddle expert has ever been able to equal him in the preparation of this supreme delicacy.

Everything was worked out on a very definite schedule, and it was truly a wonderful sight to see the big griddle being put to its daily use. Along in the afternoon every day a gang of three hundred flapjack cooks would start getting down the flour and fixin's from the elevators, start the mixers going and stir up the batter under the careful supervision of the boss baker. Meanwhile, as the batter was being mixed, the cook boys would have to grease the griddle. This they did by strapping whole hams or sides of bacon on their feet and skating around over the hot surface.

When the batter was all ready and the greasing done, some one on the edge would blow a whistle, and so big was the griddle that it took four minutes for the sound to get across. At this signal, all the cook boys would skate to the edge and climb high on the fence that had been fixed for that purpose. A cook would then trip the chute from the mixers, and out would roll a wave of flapjack batter ten feet high. Any poor cook boy who hadn't climbed out of the way, and was overtaken by the spreading batter, was in the worst kind of luck, for he would be found later in the flapjack just like a raisin in a cake.

Paul had a hard time at first figuring out how to flip the flapjack over onto its other side so that both sides of it would be cooked the same. Everyone has, of course, seen flapjacks flipped up in the air out of a skillet, so that when they come down again they have turned completely over and the undone side has a chance to get browned in its turn. Of course the big griddle and the flapjack on it were far too heavy for any wrist to flip in the ordinary manner, and so for a while everybody had to eat flapjack that was done only on one side. Paul

162

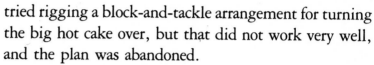

tried rigging a block-and-tackle arrangement for turning the big hot cake over, but that did not work very well, and the plan was abandoned.

At last he hit on the scheme of flipping it over with dynamite, which plan worked out so well that it was used from that time on. Whenever one side of the flapjack became done, he would explode a ton or so of dynamite under it, and away up in the air the big cake would sail until it was almost out of sight. By putting a few more sticks under one side than under the other, he made sure that it would turn over while in the air, and so nicely did he calculate the exact amount of explosive to use each time that when the flapjack came down again it landed exactly on the griddle with the brown side uppermost.

After this, Paul's men never had any cause for kicking about the flapjacks in the Red River Camp, except occasionally when a cook boy was caught by the batter and served up in the hot cake—which usually didn't happen more than two or three times a month.

*H*ere *is a humorous story by Mark Twain, one of America's most popular authors. Twain used his own experiences as a boy growing up in Hannibal, Missouri, as material for his writing. He modeled the character Tom Sawyer after himself and used his memories of friends and relatives for other characters, including Aunt Polly, Huck Finn, and Becky Thatcher. Twain wrote about these and other colorful characters in* The Adventures of Tom Sawyer *and* The Adventures of Huckleberry Finn. *He also described his experiences as a riverboat pilot in the book* Life on the Mississippi.

The Cat and the Pain-Killer

Mark Twain

The Adventures of Tom Sawyer tells the story of a boy who grew up in a small town on the Mississippi River about 100 years ago. Tom and his friends really did have adventures— they got lost in a cave, they were witnesses in a murder trial, and one time they even disappeared on an island in the river. During all this, Tom lived with his Aunt Polly who, at times, found Tom's shenanigans more than she could handle.

TOM'S MIND HAD DRIFTED away from its secret troubles. It had found a new and weighty matter to interest itself about. Becky Thatcher had stopped coming to school. Tom had struggled with his pride a few days, and tried to "whistle her down the wind," but failed. He began to find himself hanging around her father's house, nights, and feeling very miserable. She was ill. What if she should die? There was distraction in the thought. He no longer took an interest in war, nor even in piracy. He put his hoop away and his bat; there was no joy in them any more. His aunt was becoming concerned.

She began to try all manner of remedies on him. She was one of those people who are infatuated with patent medicines and all newfangled methods of producing health or mending it. She was an inveterate experimenter in these things. When something fresh in this line came out she was in a fever, right away, to try it—not on herself, for she was never ailing, but on anybody else that came handy. She was a subscriber for all the "Health" periodicals. The solemn ignorance they were inflated with was breath to her nostrils. She never observed that her health journals of the current month customarily upset everything they had recommended the month before. She was as simple-hearted and honest as the day is long and so she was an easy victim.

The water treatment was new now, and Tom's low condition was a windfall to her. She had him out at daylight every morning, stood him up in the woodshed and drowned him with a deluge of cold water. Then she scrubbed him down with a towel like a file, and so brought him to. Then she rolled him up in a wet sheet and put him away under blankets till she sweated his soul clean and "the yellow stains of it came through his pores"—as Tom said.

Yet notwithstanding all this, the boy grew more and more melancholy and pale and dejected. She added hot baths, sitz baths, shower baths, and plunges. The boy remained as dismal as a hearse. She began to assist the water with a slim oatmeal diet and blister-plasters. She calculated his capacity as she would a jug's, and filled him up every day with quack cure-alls.

Tom had become indifferent to persecution by this time. This phase filled the old lady's heart with consternation. This indifference must be broken up at any cost. Now she heard of Pain-killer for the first time. She ordered a lot at once. She tasted it and was filled with gratitude. It was simply fire in a liquid form. She dropped the water treatment and everything else, and pinned her faith to Pain-killer. She gave Tom a teaspoonful and watched with the deepest anxiety for the result. Her troubles were instantly at rest, her soul at peace again, for the "indifference" was broken up. The boy could not have shown a wilder, heartier interest if she had built a fire under him.

Tom felt that it was time to wake up. This sort of life might be romantic enough, in his blighted condition, but it was getting to have too little sentiment and too much distracting variety about it. So he thought over various plans for relief, and finally hit upon that of professing to be fond of Pain-killer. He asked for it so often that he became a nuisance, and his aunt ended by telling him to help himself and quit bothering her. If it had been Sid, she would have had no misgivings

to alloy her delight; but since it was Tom, she watched the bottle clandestinely. She found that the medicine did really diminish, but it did not occur to her that the boy was mending the health of a crack in the sitting room floor with it.

One day Tom was in the act of dosing the crack when his aunt's yellow cat came along, purring, eyeing the teaspoon avariciously, and begging for a taste. Tom said: "Don't ask for it unless you want it, Peter."

But Peter signified that he did want it.

"You better make sure."

Peter was sure.

"Now you've asked for it, and I'll give it to you, because there ain't anything mean about *me*. But if you find you don't like it, you mustn't blame anybody but your own self."

Peter was agreeable. So Tom pried his mouth open and poured down the Pain-killer. Peter sprang a couple of yards in the air, and then delivered a war whoop and set off round and round the room, banging against furniture, upsetting flower pots, and making general havoc. Next he rose on his hind feet and pranced around, in a frenzy of enjoyment, with his head over his shoulder and his voice proclaiming his unappeasable happiness. Then he went tearing around the house again, spreading chaos and destruction in his path. Aunt Polly entered in time to see him throw a few double somersaults, deliver a final mighty hurrah, and sail through the open window, carrying the rest of the flower pots with him. The old lady stood petrified with astonishment, peering over her glasses. Tom lay on the floor expiring with laughter.

"Tom, what on earth ails that cat?"

"*I* don't know, aunt," gasped the boy.

"Why, I never see anything like it. What *did* make him act so?"

" 'Deed I don't know, Aunt Polly. Cats always act so when they're having a good time."

"They do, do they?" There was something in the tone that made Tom apprehensive.

"Yes'm. That is, I believe they do."

"You *do*?"

"Yes'm!"

The old lady was bending down, Tom watching, with interest emphasized by anxiety. Too late he divined her drift. The handle of the telltale teaspoon was visible under the bed valance. Aunt Polly took it, held it up. Tom winced, and dropped his eyes. Aunt Polly raised him by the usual handle—his ear—and cracked his head soundly with her thimble.

"Now, sir, what did you want to treat that poor dumb beast so for?"

"I done it out of pity for him—because he hadn't any aunt."

"Hadn't any aunt!—you numskull. What has that got to do with it?"

"Heaps. Because if he'd 'a' had one she'd 'a' burnt him out herself! She'd 'a' roasted his bowels out of him 'thout any more feeling than if he was a human!"

Aunt Polly felt a sudden pang of remorse. This was putting the thing in a new light. What was cruelty to a cat *might* be cruelty to a boy, too. She began to soften; she felt sorry. Her eyes watered a little, and she put her hand on Tom's head and said in the gentlest possible way she could manage:

"I was meaning for the best, Tom. And, Tom it *did* do you good."

Tom looked up in her face with just a perceptible twinkle peeping through his gravity.

"I know you was meaning for the best, auntie, and

so was I with Peter. It done *him* good, too. I never see him get around so since—"

"Oh, go 'long with you, Tom, before you aggravate me again. And you try and see if you can't be a good boy, for once, and you needn't take any more medicine."

This is a delightful story from the pen of Rudyard Kipling, one of England's great writers. This clever and imaginative yarn about how the elephant got his trunk is from Kipling's book Just So Stories. *"The Elephant's Child" is set in Africa, but many of Kipling's novels, poems, and stories are set in India, where he was born and lived for a number of years. His other collections of stories for young people include* The Jungle Book *and* The Second Jungle Book.

The Elephant's Child

Rudyard Kipling

IN THE HIGH AND FAR-OFF TIMES the Elephant, O Best Beloved, had no trunk. He had only a blackish, bulgy nose, as big as a boot, that he could wriggle about from side to side; but he couldn't pick up things with it. But there was one Elephant—a new Elephant— an Elephant's Child—who was full of 'satiable curtiosity, and that means he asked ever so many questions. *And* he lived in Africa, and he filled all Africa with his 'satiable curtiosities. He asked his tall aunt, the Ostrich, why her tail feathers grew just so, and his tall aunt the Ostrich spanked him with her hard, hard claw. He asked his tall uncle, the Giraffe, what made his skin spotty, and his tall uncle, the Giraffe, spanked him with his hard, hard hoof. And still he was just full of 'satiable curtiosity! He asked his broad aunt, the Hippopotamus, why her eyes were red, and his broad aunt, the Hippopotamus, spanked him with her broad, broad hoof; and he asked his hairy uncle, the Baboon, why melons tasted just so, and his hairy uncle, the Baboon, spanked him with his hairy, hairy paw. And *still* he was full of 'satiable curtiosity! He asked questions about everything that he saw, or heard, or felt, or smelt, or touched, and all his uncles and his aunts spanked him. And still he was full of 'satiable curtiosity!

One fine morning in the middle of the Precession of the Equinoxes this 'satiable Elephant's Child asked a new fine question that he had never asked before. He asked, "What does the Crocodile have for dinner?" Then everybody said, "Hush!" in a loud and dreadful tone, and they spanked him immediately and directly, without stopping, for a long time.

By and by, when that was finished, he came upon Kolokolo Bird sitting in the middle of a wait-a-bit thornbush, and he said, "My father has spanked me, and my mother has spanked me; all my aunts and uncles have spanked me for my 'satiable curtiosity; and *still* I want to know what the Crocodile has for dinner!"

Then Kolokolo Bird said, with a mournful cry, "Go to the banks of the great gray-green, greasy Limpopo River, all set about with fever trees, and find out."

That very next morning, when there was nothing left of the Equinoxes, because the Precession had preceded according to precedent, this 'satiable Elephant's Child took a hundred pounds of bananas (the little short red kind), and a hundred pounds of sugarcane (the long purple kind), and seventeen melons (the greeny-crackly kind), and said to all his dear families, "Good-bye. I am going to the great gray-green, greasy Limpopo River, all set about with fever trees, to find out what the Crocodile has for dinner." And they all spanked him once more for luck, though he asked them most politely to stop.

Then he went away, a little warm, but not at all astonished, eating melons, and throwing the rind about, because he could not pick it up.

He went from Graham's Town to Kimberley, and from Kimberley to Khama's Country, and from Khama's Country he went east by north, eating melons all the time, till at last he came to the banks of the great gray-green, greasy Limpopo River, all set about with fever trees, precisely as Kolokolo Bird had said.

Now you must know and understand, O Best Beloved, that till that very week, and day, and hour, and minute, this 'satiable Elephant's Child had never seen a Crocodile, and did not know what one was like. It was all his 'satiable curtiosity.

The first thing that he found was a Bi-Colored-Python-Rock-Snake curled round a rock.

" 'Scuse me," said the Elephant's Child most politely, "but have you seen such a thing as a Crocodile in these promiscuous parts?"

"*Have* I seen a Crocodile?" said the Bi-Colored-Python-Rock-Snake, in a voice of dreadful scorn. "What will you ask me next?"

" 'Scuse me," said the Elephant's Child, "but could you kindly tell me what he has for dinner?"

Then the Bi-Colored-Python-Rock-Snake uncoiled himself very quickly from the rock, and spanked the Elephant's Child with his scalesome, flailsome tail.

"That is odd," said the Elephant's Child, "because my father and my mother, and my uncle and my aunt, not to mention my other aunt, the Hippopotamus, and my other uncle, the Baboon, have all spanked me for my 'satiable curtiosity—and I suppose this is the same thing."

So he said good-bye very politely to the Bi-Colored-Python-Rock-Snake, and helped to coil him up on the rock again, and went on, a little warm, but not at all astonished, eating melons, and throwing the rind about, because he could not pick it up, till he trod on what he thought was a log of wood at the very edge of the great gray-green, greasy Limpopo River, all set about with fever trees.

But it was really the Crocodile, O Best Beloved, and the Crocodile winked one eye—like this!

" 'Scuse me," said the Elephant's Child most politely, "but do you happen to have seen a Crocodile in these promiscuous parts?"

Then the Crocodile winked the other eye, and lifted half his tail out of the mud; and the Elephant's Child stepped back most politely, because he did not wish to be spanked again.

"Come hither, Little One," said the Crocodile. "Why do you ask such things?"

" 'Scuse me," said the Elephant's Child most politely, "but my father has spanked me, my mother has spanked me, not to mention my tall aunt, the Ostrich, and my tall uncle, the Giraffe, who can kick ever so hard, as well as my broad aunt, the Hippopotamus, and my hairy uncle, the Baboon, *and* including the Bi-Colored-Python-Rock-Snake, with the scalesome, flailsome tail, just up the bank, who spanks harder than any of them; and *so,* if it's quite all the same to you, I don't want to be spanked any more."

"Come hither, Little One," said the Crocodile, "for I am the Crocodile," and he wept crocodile tears to show it was quite true.

Then the Elephant's Child grew all breathless, and panted, and kneeled down on the bank and said, "You are the very person I have been looking for all these long days. Will you please tell me what you have for dinner?"

"Come hither, Little One," said the Crocodile, "and

I'll whisper."

Then the Elephant's Child put his head down close to the Crocodile's musky, tusky mouth, and the Crocodile caught him by his little nose, which up to that very week, day, hour, and minute, had been no bigger than a boot, though much more useful.

"I think," said the Crocodile—and he said it between his teeth, like this—"I think today I will begin with Elephant's Child!"

At this, O Best Beloved, the Elephant's Child was much annoyed, and he said, speaking through his nose, like this, "Led go! You are hurtig be!"

Then the Bi-Colored-Python-Rock-Snake scuffled down from the bank and said, "My young friend, if you do not now, immediately and instantly, pull as hard as ever you can, it is my opinion that your acquaintance in the large-pattern leather ulster" (and by this he meant the Crocodile) "will jerk you into yonder limpid stream before you can say Jack Robinson."

This is the way Bi-Colored-Python-Rock-Snakes always talk.

Then the Elephant's Child sat back on his little haunches, and pulled, and pulled, and pulled, and his nose began to stretch. And the Crocodile floundered into the water, making it all creamy with great sweeps of his tail, and *he* pulled, and pulled, and pulled.

And the Elephant's Child's nose kept on stretching; and the Elephant's Child spread all his little four legs and pulled, and pulled, and pulled, and his nose kept on stretching; and the Crocodile threshed his tail like an oar, and *he* pulled, and pulled, and pulled, and at each pull the Elephant's Child's nose grew longer and longer—and it hurt him hijjus!

Then the Elephant's Child felt his legs slipping, and he said through his nose, which was now nearly five feet long, "This is too butch for be!"

Then the Bi-Colored-Python-Rock-Snake came down from the bank, and knotted himself in a double clove hitch round the Elephant's Child's hind legs, and said, "Rash and inexperienced traveler, we will now seriously devote ourselves to a little high tension, because if we do not, it is my impression that yonder self-propelling man-of-war with the armor-plated upper deck" (and by this, O Best Beloved, he meant the Crocodile) "will permanently vitiate your future career."

That is the way all Bi-Colored-Python-Rock-Snakes always talk.

So he pulled, and the Elephant's Child pulled, and the Crocodile pulled; but the Elephant's Child and the Bi-Colored-Python-Rock-Snake pulled hardest; and at last the Crocodile let go of the Elephant's Child's nose with a plop that you could hear all up and down the Limpopo.

Then the Elephant's Child sat down most hard and sudden; but first he was careful to say "Thank you" to the Bi-Colored-Python-Rock-Snake; and next he was kind to his poor pulled nose, and wrapped it all up in cool banana leaves, and hung it in the great gray-green, greasy Limpopo to cool.

"What are you doing that for?" said the Bi-Colored-Python-Rock-Snake.

" 'Scuse me," said the Elephant's Child, "but my nose is badly out of shape, and I am waiting for it to shrink."

"Then you will have to wait a long time," said the Bi-Colored-Python-Rock-Snake. "Some people do not know what is good for them."

The Elephant's Child sat there for three days waiting for his nose to shrink. But it never grew any shorter, and, besides, it made him squint. For, O Best Beloved, you will see and understand that the Crocodile had pulled it out into a really truly trunk same as all Elephants have today.

At the end of the third day a fly came and stung him on the shoulder, and before he knew what he was doing he lifted up his trunk and hit that fly dead with the end of it.

" 'Vantage number one!" said the Bi-Colored-Python-Rock-Snake. "You couldn't have done that with a mere-smear nose. Try and eat a little now."

Before he thought what he was doing the Elephant's Child put out his trunk and plucked a large bundle of grass, dusted it clean against his forelegs, and stuffed it into his own mouth.

" 'Vantage number two!" said the Bi-Colored-Python-Rock-Snake. "You couldn't have done that with a mere-

180

smear nose. Don't you think the sun is very hot here?"

"It is," said the Elephant's Child, and before he thought what he was doing he schlooped up a schloop of mud from the banks of the great gray-green, greasy Limpopo, and slapped it on his head, where it made a cool schloopy-sloshy mudcap all trickly behind his ears.

" 'Vantage number three!" said the Bi-Colored-Python-Rock-Snake. "You couldn't have done that with a mere-smear nose. Now how do you feel about being spanked again?"

" 'Scuse me," said the Elephant's Child, "but I should not like it at all."

"How would you like to spank somebody?" said the Bi-Colored-Python-Rock-Snake.

"I should like it very much indeed," said the Elephant's Child.

"Well," said the Bi-Colored-Python-Rock-Snake, "you will find that new nose of yours very useful to spank people with."

"Thank you," said the Elephant's Child, "I'll remember that; and now I think I'll go home to all my dear families and try."

So the Elephant's Child went home across Africa frisking and whisking his trunk. When he wanted fruit to eat he pulled fruit down from a tree instead of waiting for it to fall as he used to do. When he wanted grass he plucked grass up from the ground instead of going on his knees as he used to do. When the flies bit him he broke off the branch of a tree and used it as a fly whisk; and he made himself a new, cool, slushy-squshy mudcap whenever the sun was hot. When he felt lonely walking through Africa he sang to himself down his trunk, and the noise was louder than several brass bands. He went especially out of his way to find a broad Hippopotamus (she was no relation of his), and he spanked her very hard, to make sure that the Bi-Colored-Python-Rock-Snake had spoken the truth about his new trunk. The rest of the time he picked up the melon rinds that he had dropped on his way to the Limpopo—for he was a Tidy Pachyderm.

One dark evening he came back to all his dear families, and he coiled up his trunk and said, "How do you do?" They were very glad to see him, and immediately said, "Come here and be spanked now for your 'satiable curtiosity."

"Pooh," said the Elephant's Child. "I don't think you peoples know anything about spanking; but *I* do, and I'll show you."

Then he uncurled his trunk and knocked two of his dear brothers head over heels.

"O Bananas!" said they, "Where did you learn that trick, and what have you done to your nose?"

"I got a new one from the Crocodile on the banks of the great gray-green, greasy Limpopo River," said the Elephant's Child. "I asked him what he had for dinner, and he gave me this to keep."

"It looks very ugly," said his hairy uncle, the Baboon.

"It does," said the Elephant's Child. "But it's very useful," and he picked up his hairy uncle, the Baboon, by one hairy leg, and hove him into a hornets' nest.

Then that bad Elephant's Child spanked all his dear families for a long time, till they were very warm and greatly astonished. He pulled out his tall Ostrich aunt's tail feathers; and he caught his tall uncle, the Giraffe, by the hindleg, and dragged him through a thornbush;

and he shouted at his broad aunt, the Hippopotamus, and blew bubbles into her ear when she was sleeping in the water after meals; but he never let any one touch Kolokolo Bird.

At last things grew so exciting that his dear families went off one by one in a hurry to the banks of the great gray-green, greasy Limpopo River, all set about with fever trees, to borrow new noses from the Crocodile. When they came back nobody spanked anybody any more; and ever since that day, O Best Beloved, all the Elephants you will ever see, besides all those that you won't, have trunks precisely like the trunk of the 'satiable Elephant's Child.

I KEEP six honest serving-men;
   (They taught me all I knew)
Their names are What and Why and When
   And How and Where and Who.
I send them over land and sea,
   I send them east and west;
But after they have worked for me,
   I give them all a rest.
I let them rest from nine till five,
   For I am busy then,
As well as breakfast, lunch, and tea,
   For they are hungry men:
But different folk have different views:
   I know a person small—
She keeps ten million serving-men,
   Who get no rest at all
She sends 'em abroad on her own affairs,
   From the second she opens her eyes—
One million Hows, two million Wheres
   And seven million Whys!

One day, while window shopping in town, Sally and Sam noticed something new in the window of the pet shop. It was a small, pink-nosed rabbit. But it did not move, not even one little whisker.

"It isn't real," Sally said, disappointed at the discovery of this fact.

"Well, maybe all it needs is a child to love it enough. Then it will become real."

"Oh, Sam, you mean like in that story?"

"Yes," Sam replied. " 'The Velveteen Rabbit.' That little rabbit became real, just like Pinocchio the puppet became real."

"Do you think the Velveteen Rabbit really came to life, Sam?"

"In the world of books, anything *is* possible!" Sam replied, laughing.

The Velveteen Rabbit
or How Toys Become Real

Margery Williams

THERE WAS ONCE A VELVETEEN RABBIT, and in the beginning he was really splendid. He was fat and bunchy, as a rabbit should be; his coat was spotted brown and white, he had real thread whiskers, and his ears were lined with pink sateen. On Christmas morning, when he sat wedged in the top of the Boy's stocking, with a sprig of holly between his paws, the effect was charming.

There were other things in the stocking, nuts and oranges and a toy engine, and chocolate almonds and a clockwork mouse, but the Rabbit was quite the best of all. For at least two hours the Boy loved him, and then Aunts and Uncles came to dinner, and there was a great rustling of tissue paper and unwrapping of parcels, and in the excitement of looking at all the new presents the Velveteen Rabbit was forgotten.

For a long time he lived in the toy cupboard or on the nursery floor, and no one thought very much about him. He was naturally shy, and being only made of velveteen, some of the more expensive toys quite

snubbed him. The mechanical toys were very superior, and looked down upon everyone else; they were full of modern ideas, and pretended they were real. The model boat, who had lived through two seasons and lost most of his paint, caught the tone from them and never missed an opportunity of referring to his rigging in technical terms. The Rabbit could not claim to be a model of anything, for he didn't know that real rabbits existed; he thought they were all stuffed with sawdust like himself, and he understood that sawdust was quite out of date and should never be mentioned in modern circles. Even Timothy, the jointed wooden lion, who was made by the disabled soldiers, and should have had broader views, put on airs and pretended he was connected with Government. Between them all the poor little Rabbit was made to feel himself very insignificant and commonplace, and the only person who was kind to him at all was the Skin Horse.

The Skin Horse had lived longer in the nursery than any of the others. He was so old that his brown coat was bald in patches and showed the seams underneath, and most of the hairs in his tail had been pulled out to string bead necklaces. He was wise, for he had seen a long succession of mechanical toys arrive to boast and swagger, and by and by break their mainsprings and pass away, and he knew that they were only toys, and would never turn into anything else. For nursery magic is very strange and wonderful, and only those playthings that are old and wise and experienced like the Skin Horse understand all about it.

"What is REAL?" asked the Rabbit one day, when they were lying side by side near the nursery fender, before Nana came to tidy the room. "Does it mean having things that buzz inside you and a stick-out handle?"

"Real isn't how you are made," said the Skin Horse. "It's a thing that happens to you. When a child loves you for a long, long time, not just to play with, but REALLY loves you, then you become Real."

"Does it hurt?" asked the Rabbit.

"Sometimes," said the Skin Horse, for he was always truthful. "When you are Real you don't mind being hurt."

"Does it happen all at once, like being wound up," he asked, "or bit by bit?"

"It doesn't happen all at once," said the Skin Horse. "You become. It takes a long time. That's why it doesn't often happen to people who break easily, or have sharp edges, or who have to be carefully kept. Generally, by the time you are Real, most of your hair has been loved off, and your eyes drop out and you get loose in the joints and very shabby. But these things don't matter at all, because once you are Real you can't be ugly, except to people who don't understand."

"I suppose *you* are Real?" said the Rabbit. And then he wished he had not said it, for he thought the Skin Horse might be sensitive. But the Skin Horse only smiled.

"The Boy's Uncle made me Real," he said. "That was a great many years ago; but once you are Real you can't become unreal again. It lasts for always."

The Rabbit sighed. He thought it would be a long time before this magic called Real happened to him. He longed to become Real, to know what it felt like; and yet the idea of growing shabby and losing his eyes and whiskers was rather sad. He wished that he could become it without these uncomfortable things happening to him.

There was a person called Nana who ruled the nursery. Sometimes she took no notice of the playthings lying about, and sometimes, for no reason whatever, she went swooping about like a great wind and hustled them away in cupboards. She called this "tidying up," and the playthings all hated it, especially the tin ones. The Rabbit didn't mind it so much, for wherever he was thrown he came down soft.

One evening, when the Boy was going to bed, he couldn't find the china dog that always slept with him.

Nana was in a hurry, and it was too much trouble to hunt for china dogs at bedtime, so she simply looked about her, and seeing that the toy cupboard door stood open, she made a swoop.

"Here," she said, "take your old Bunny! He'll do to sleep with you!" And she dragged the Rabbit out by one ear, and put him into the Boy's arms.

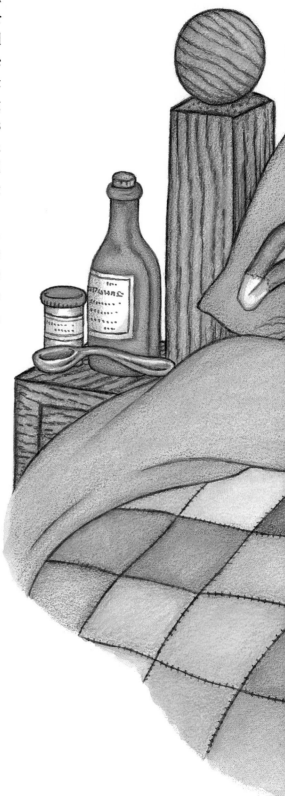

That night, and for many nights after, the Velveteen Rabbit slept in the Boy's bed. At first he found it rather uncomfortable, for the Boy hugged him very tight, and sometimes he rolled over on him, and sometimes he pushed him so far under the pillow that the Rabbit could scarcely breathe. And he missed, too, those long moonlight hours in the nursery, when all the house was silent, and his talks with the Skin Horse. But very soon he grew to like it, for the Boy used to talk to him, and made nice tunnels for him, under the bedclothes, that he said were like the burrows the real rabbits lived in. And they had splendid games together, in whispers, when Nana had gone away to her supper and left the night light burning on the mantelpiece. And when the Boy dropped off to sleep, the Rabbit would snuggle down close under his little warm chin and dream, with the Boy's hands clasped close round him all night long.

And so time went on, and the little Rabbit was very happy—so happy that he never noticed how his beautiful velveteen fur was getting shabbier and shabbier, and his tail coming unsewn, and all the pink rubbed off his nose where the Boy had kissed him.

Spring came, and they had long days in the garden, for wherever the Boy went the Rabbit went too. He had rides in the wheelbarrow, and picnics on the grass, and lovely fairy huts built for him under the raspberry canes behind the flower border. And once, when the Boy was called away suddenly to go out to tea, the Rabbit was left out on the lawn until long after dusk, and Nana had to come and look for him with the candle because the Boy couldn't go to sleep unless he was there. He was wet through with the dew and quite earthy from diving into the burrows the Boy had made for him in the flower bed, and Nana grumbled as she rubbed him off with a corner of her apron.

"You must have your old Bunny!" she said. "Fancy all that fuss for a toy!"

The Boy sat up in bed and stretched out his hands.

"Give me my Bunny!" he said. "You mustn't say that. He isn't a toy. He's REAL!"

When the little Rabbit heard that, he was happy, for he knew that what the Skin Horse had said was true at last. The nursery magic had happened to him, and he was a toy no longer. He was Real. The Boy himself had said it.

That night he was almost too happy to sleep, and so much love stirred in his little sawdust heart that it almost burst. And into his boot-button eyes, that had long ago lost their polish, there came a look of wisdom and beauty, so that even Nana noticed it next morning when she picked him up, and said, "I declare if that old Bunny hasn't got quite a knowing expression!"

That was a wonderful Summer!

Near the house where they lived there was a wood, and in the long June evenings the Boy liked to go there after tea to play. He took the Velveteen Rabbit with him, and before he wandered off to pick flowers, or play at brigands among the trees, he always made the Rabbit a little nest somewhere among the bracken, where he would be quite cozy, for he was a kindhearted little boy and he liked Bunny to be comfortable. One evening, while the Rabbit was lying there alone, watching the ants that ran to and fro between his velvet paws in the grass, he saw two strange beings creep out of the tall bracken near him.

They were rabbits like himself, but quite furry and brand new. They must have been very well made, for their seams didn't show at all, and they changed shape in a queer way when they moved; one minute they were long and thin and the next minute fat and bunchy, instead of always staying the same like he did. Their feet padded softly on the ground, and they crept quite close to him, twitching their noses, while the Rabbit stared hard to see where the clockwork stuck out, for he knew that people who jump generally have something to wind them up. But he couldn't see it. They were evidently a new kind of rabbit altogether.

They stared at him, and the little Rabbit stared back. And all the time their noses twitched.

"Why don't you get up and play with us?" one of them asked.

"I don't feel like it," said the Rabbit, for he didn't want to explain that he had no clockwork.

"Ho!" said the furry rabbit. "It's as easy as anything." And he gave a big hop sideways and stood on his hind legs.

"I don't believe you can!" he said.

"I can!" said the little Rabbit. "I can jump higher than anything!" He meant when the Boy threw him, but of course he didn't want to say so.

"Can you hop on your hind legs?" asked the furry rabbit.

That was a dreadful question, for the Velveteen Rabbit had no hind legs at all! The back of him was made all in one piece, like a pincushion. He sat still in the bracken, and hoped that the other rabbits would never notice.

"I don't want to!" he said again.

But the wild rabbits have very sharp eyes. And this one stretched out his neck and looked.

"He hasn't got any hind legs!" he called out. "Fancy a rabbit without any hind legs!" And he began to laugh.

"I have!" cried the little Rabbit. "I have got hind legs! I am sitting on them!"

"Then stretch them out and show me, like this!" said the wild rabbit. And he began to whirl around and dance, till the little Rabbit got quite dizzy.

"I don't like dancing," he said. "I'd rather sit still!"

But all the while he was longing to dance, for a funny new tickly feeling ran through him, and he felt he would give anything in the world to be able to jump about like these rabbits did.

The strange rabbit stopped dancing, and came quite close. He came so close this time that his long whiskers

brushed the Velveteen Rabbit's ear, and then he wrinkled his nose suddenly and flattened his ears and jumped backward.

"He doesn't smell right!" he exclaimed. "He isn't a rabbit at all! He isn't real!"

"I *am* Real!" said the little Rabbit. "I am Real! The Boy said so!" And he nearly began to cry.

Just then there was a sound of footsteps, and the Boy ran past near them, and with a stamp of feet and a flash of white tails the two strange rabbits disappeared.

"Come back and play with me!" called the little Rabbit. "Oh, do come back! I *know* I am Real!"

But there was no answer, only the little ants ran to and fro, and the bracken swayed gently where the two strangers had passed. The Velveteen Rabbit was all alone.

"Oh, dear!" he thought. "Why did they run away like that? Why couldn't they stop and talk to me?"

For a long time he lay very still, watching the bracken, and hoping that they would come back. But they never returned, and presently the sun sank lower and the little white moths fluttered out, and the Boy came and carried him home.

Weeks passed, and the little Rabbit grew very old and shabby, but the Boy loved him just as much. He loved him so hard that he loved all his whiskers off, and the pink lining to his ears turned grey, and his brown spots faded. He even began to lose his shape, and he scarcely looked like a rabbit any more, except to the Boy. To him he was always beautiful, and that was all that the little Rabbit cared about. He didn't mind how he looked to other people, because the nursery magic had made him Real, and when you are Real shabbiness doesn't matter.

And then, one day, the Boy was ill.

His face grew very flushed, and he talked in his sleep, and his little body was so hot that it burned the Rabbit when he held him close. Strange people came and went in the nursery, and a light burned all night, and through it all the little Velveteen Rabbit lay there, hidden from sight under the bedclothes, and he never stirred, for he was afraid that if they found him some one might take him away, and he knew that the Boy needed him.

It was a long weary time, for the Boy was too ill to play, and the little Rabbit found it rather dull with nothing to do all day long. But he snuggled down patiently, and looked forward to the time when the Boy should be well again, and they would go out in the garden among the flowers and the butterflies and play splendid games in the raspberry thicket like they used to. All sorts of delightful things he planned, and while the Boy lay half asleep he crept up close to the pillow and whispered them in his ear. And presently the fever turned, and the Boy got better. He was able to sit up

in bed and look at picture books, while the little Rabbit cuddled close at his side. And one day, they let him get up and dress.

It was a bright, sunny morning, and the windows stood wide open. They had carried the Boy out on to the balcony, wrapped in a shawl, and the little Rabbit lay tangled up among the bedclothes, thinking.

The Boy was going to the seaside tomorrow. Everything was arranged, and now it only remained to carry out the doctor's orders. They talked about it all, while the little Rabbit lay under the bedclothes, with just his head peeping out, and listened. The room was to be disinfected, and all the books and toys that the Boy had played with in bed must be burnt.

"Hurrah!" thought the little Rabbit. "Tomorrow we shall go to the seaside!" For the Boy had often talked of the seaside, and he wanted very much to see the big waves coming in and to see the tiny crabs and the sand castles.

Just then Nana caught sight of him.

"How about his old Bunny?" she asked.

"*That?*" said the doctor. "Why, it's a mass of scarlet fever germs!—Burn it at once. What? Nonsense! Get him a new one. He mustn't have that any more!"

And so the little Rabbit was put into a sack with the old picture books and a lot of rubbish, and carried out to the end of the garden behind the fowl house. That was a fine place to make a bonfire, only the gardener was too busy just then to attend to it. He had the potatoes to dig and the green peas to gather, but next morning he promised to come quite early and burn the whole lot.

That night the Boy slept in a different bedroom, and he had a new bunny to sleep with him. It was a splendid bunny, all white plush with real glass eyes, but the Boy was too excited to care very much about it. For tomorrow he was going to the seaside, and that in itself was such a wonderful thing that he could think of nothing else.

And while the Boy was asleep, dreaming of the sea-side, the little Rabbit lay among the old picture books in the corner behind the fowl house, and he felt very lonely. The sack had been left untied, and so by wriggling a bit he was able to get his head through the opening and look out. He was shivering a little, for he had always been used to sleeping in a proper bed, and by this time his coat had worn so thin and threadbare from hugging that it was no longer any protection to him. Nearby he could see the thicket of raspberry canes, growing tall and close like a tropical jungle, in whose shadow he had played with the Boy on bygone mornings. He thought of those long sunlit hours in the garden—how happy they were—and a great sadness came over him. He seemed to see them all pass before him, each more beautiful than the other, the fairy huts in the flower bed, the quiet evenings in the wood when he lay in the bracken and the little ants ran over his paws; the wonderful day when he first knew that he was Real. He thought of the Skin Horse, so wise and gentle, and all that he had told him. Of what use was it to be loved and lose one's beauty and become Real if it all ended like this? And a tear, a real tear, trickled down his little shabby velvet nose and fell to the ground.

And then a strange thing happened. For where the tear had fallen a flower grew out of the ground, a mysterious flower, not at all like any that grew in the garden. It had slender green leaves the color of emeralds, and in the center of the leaves a blossom like a golden cup. It was so beautiful that the little Rabbit forgot to cry, and just lay there watching it. And presently the blossom opened, and out of it there stepped a fairy.

She was quite the loveliest fairy in the whole world. Her dress was of pearl and dewdrops, and there were flowers round her neck and in her hair, and her face was like the most perfect flower of all. And she came close to the little Rabbit and gathered him up in her arms and kissed him on his velveteen nose that was all

damp from crying.

"Little Rabbit," she said, "don't you know who I am?"

The Rabbit looked up at her, and it seemed to him that he had seen her face before, but he couldn't think where.

"I am the nursery magic Fairy," she said. "I take care of all the playthings that the children have loved. When they are old and worn out and the children don't need them any more, then I come and take them away with me and turn them into Real."

"Wasn't I Real before?" asked the little Rabbit.

"You were Real to the Boy," the Fairy said, "because he loved you. Now you shall be Real to everyone."

And she held the little Rabbit close in her arms and flew with him into the wood.

It was light now, for the moon had risen. All the forest was beautiful, and the fronds of the bracken shone like frosted silver. In the open glade between the tree trunks the wild rabbits danced with their shadows on the velvet grass, but when they saw the Fairy they all stopped dancing and stood round in a ring to stare at her.

"I've brought you a new playfellow," the Fairy said. "You must be very kind to him and teach him all he needs to know in Rabbitland, for he is going to live with you for ever and ever!"

And she kissed the little Rabbit again and put him down on the grass.

"Run and play, little Rabbit!" she said.

But the little Rabbit sat quite still for a moment and never moved. For when he saw all the wild rabbits dancing around him he suddenly remembered about his hind legs, and he didn't want them to see that he was made all in one piece. He did not know that when the Fairy kissed him that last time she had changed him altogether. And he might have sat there a long time, too shy to move, if just then something hadn't tickled his nose, and before he thought what he was doing he lifted his hind toe to scratch it.

And he found that he actually had hind legs! Instead of dingy velveteen he had brown fur, soft and shiny, his ears twitched by themselves, and his whiskers were so long that they brushed the grass. He gave one leap and the joy of using those hind legs was so great that he went springing about the turf on them, jumping sideways and whirling round as the others did, and he grew so excited that when at last he did stop to look for the Fairy she had gone.

He was a Real Rabbit at last, at home with the other rabbits.

Autumn passed and Winter, and in the Spring, when the days grew warm and sunny, the Boy went out to play in the wood behind the house. And while he was playing, two rabbits crept out from the bracken and peeped at him. One of them was brown all over, but the other had strange markings under his fur, as though long ago he had been spotted, and the spots still showed through. And about his little soft nose and his round black eyes there was something familiar, so that the Boy thought to himself:

"Why, he looks just like my old Bunny that was lost when I had scarlet fever!"

But he never knew that it really was his own Bunny, come back to look at the child who had first helped him to be Real.

Here is a chapter from the book Mary Poppins
Comes Back *by P. L. Travers, an Englishwoman whose
books have been enjoyed by young readers for many years.
Mary Poppins is a most remarkable person. She is the
governess of the Banks family, and she takes care of the
five Banks children—Jane, Michael, the twins John and
Barbara, and the baby Annabel. On this particular day
Mary Poppins and the children visit an unfamiliar part
of the park, meet an amazing Balloon Lady, and have
an impossibly exciting adventure.*

From Mary Poppins Comes Back

Balloons *and* Balloons

P. L. Travers

"I WONDER, Mary Poppins," said Mrs. Banks, hurrying into the
Nursery one morning, "if you will have time to do some shopping
for me?"

And she gave Mary Poppins a sweet, nervous smile as though she
were uncertain what the answer would be.

Mary Poppins turned from the fire where she was airing Annabel's
clothes.

"I might," she remarked, not very encouragingly.

"Oh, I see—" said Mrs. Banks and she looked more nervous than
ever.

"Or again—I might not," continued Mary Poppins, busily shaking
out a woollen jacket and hanging it over the fire-guard.

"Well—in case you *did* have time, here is the List and here is a Pound Note. And if there is any change left over you may spend it!"

Mrs. Banks put the money on the chest of drawers.

Mary Poppins said nothing. She just sniffed.

"Oh!" said Mrs. Banks, suddenly remembering something. "And the Twins must walk to-day, Mary Poppins. Robertson Ay sat down on the perambulator this morning. He mistook it for an arm-chair. So it will have to be mended. Can you manage without it—and carry Annabel?"

Mary Poppins opened her mouth and closed it again with a snap.

"I," she remarked tartly, "can manage anything—and more, if I choose."

"I—I know!" said Mrs. Banks, edging towards the door. "You are a Treasure—a perfect Treasure—an absolutely wonderful and altogether suitable Treas—" Her voice died away as she hurried down the stairs.

"And yet—and yet—I sometimes wish she wasn't!" Mrs. Banks remarked to her great-grandmother's portrait as she dusted the Drawing-room. "She makes me feel small and silly, as though I were a

little girl again. And I'm not!" Mrs. Banks tossed her head and flicked a speck of dust from the spotted cow on the mantelpiece. "I'm a very important person and the Mother of five children. She forgets that!" And she went on with her work thinking out all the things she would like to say to Mary Poppins but knowing all the time that never would she dare.

Mary Poppins put the list and the Pound Note into her bag and in no time she had pinned on her hat and was hurrying out of the house with Annabel in her arms and Jane and Michael, each holding the hand of a Twin, following as quickly as they could.

"Best foot forward, please!" she remarked, turning sternly upon them.

They quickened their pace, dragging the poor Twins with a shuffling sound along the pavement. They forgot that John's arm and Barbara's were being pulled nearly out of their sockets. Their only thought was to keep up with Mary Poppins and see what she did with the change from the Pound Note.

"Two packets of candles, four pounds of rice, three of brown sugar and six of castor; two tins of tomato soup and a hearth-brush, a pair of house-maid's gloves, half-a-stick of sealing-wax, one bag of flour, one fire-lighter, two boxes of matches, two cauliflowers and a bundle of rhubarb!"

Mary Poppins, hurrying into the first shop beyond the Park, read out the list.

The Grocer, who was fat and bald and rather short of breath, took down the order as quickly as he could.

"One bag of housemaid's gloves—" he wrote, nervously licking the wrong end of his blunt little pencil.

"Flour, I said!" Mary Poppins reminded him tartly.

The Grocer blushed as red as a mulberry.

"Oh, I'm sorry. No offense meant, I'm sure. Lovely day, isn't it? Yes. My mistake. One bag of house—er—flour."

He hurriedly scribbled it down and added—

"Two boxes of hearth-brushes—"

"Matches!" snapped Mary Poppins.

The Grocer's hands trembled on his pad.

"Oh, of course. It must be the pencil—it seems to write all the wrong things. I must get a new one. Matches, of course! And then you said—?" He looked up nervously and then down again at his little stub of pencil.

Mary Poppins, unfolded the list, read it out again in an angry, impatient voice.

"Sorry," said the Grocer, as she came to the end. "But rhubarb's off. Would damsons do?"

"Certainly not. A packet of Tapioca."

"Oh, no, Mary Poppins—not Tapioca. We had that last week," Michael reminded her.

She glanced at him and then at the Grocer and by the look in her eye they both knew that there was no hope. Tapioca it would be. The Grocer, blushing redder than ever, went away to get it.

"There won't be any change left if she goes on like

this," said Jane, watching the pile of groceries being heaped upon the counter.

"She might have enough left over for a bag of acid-drops—but that's all," Michael said mournfully, as Mary Poppins took the Pound Note out of her bag.

"Thank you," she said, as the Grocer handed her the change.

"Thank *you*!" he remarked politely, leaning his arms on the counter. He smiled at her in a manner that was meant to be pleasant and continued, "Keeps nice and fine, doesn't it?" He spoke proudly as though he, himself, had complete charge of the weather and had made it fine for her on purpose.

"We want rain!" said Mary Poppins, snapping her mouth and her hand-bag at the same time.

"That's right," said the Grocer hurriedly, trying not to offend her. "Rain's always pleasant."

"Never!" retorted Mary Poppins, tossing Annabel into a more comfortable position on her arm.

The Grocer's face fell. *Nothing* he said was right.

"I hope," he remarked, opening the door courteously for Mary Poppins, "that we shall be favoured with your further custom, Madam."

"Good-day!" Mary Poppins swept out.

The Grocer sighed.

"Here," he said, scrabbling hurriedly in a box near the door. "Take these. I meant no harm, truly I didn't. I only wanted to oblige."

Jane and Michael held out their hands. The Grocer slipped three chocolate drops into Michael's and two into Jane's.

"One for each of you, one for the two little ones and one for—" he nodded towards Mary Poppins' retreating figure—"her!"

They thanked the Grocer and hurried after Mary Poppins, munching their chocolate drops.

"What's that you're eating?" she demanded, looking at the dark rim round Michael's mouth.

"Chocolates. The Grocer gave us one each. And one for you." He held out the last drop. It was very sticky.

"Like his impudence!" said Mary Poppins, but she took the chocolate drop and ate it in two bites as though she thoroughly enjoyed it.

"Is there much change left?" enquired Michael anxiously.

"That's as may be."

She swept into the Chemist's and came out with a cake of soap, a mustard plaster, and a tube of toothpaste.

Jane and Michael, waiting with the Twins at the door, sighed heavily.

The Pound Note, they knew, was disappearing fast.

"She'll hardly have enough left over for a stamp and, even if she has, *that* won't be very interesting," said Jane.

"Now to Mr. Tip's!" snapped Mary Poppins, swinging the Chemist's packages and her bag from one hand and holding Annabel tightly with the other.

"But what can we buy *there*?" said Michael in despair. For there was not much jingle in Mary Poppins' purse.

"Coal—two tons and a half," she said, hurrying ahead.

"How much is coal?"

"Two pounds a ton."

"But—Mary Poppins! We can't buy *that*!" Michael stared at her, appalled.

"It will go on the bill."

This was such a relief to Jane and Michael that they bounded beside her, dragging John and Barbara behind them at a trot.

"Well, is that all?" Michael asked, when Mr. Tip and his coals had been left safely behind.

"Cake shop!" said Mary Poppins, examining her list and darting in at a dark door. Through the window they could see her pointing to a pile of macaroons. The assistant handed her a large bag.

"She's bought a dozen at least," said Jane sadly. Usually the sight of anybody buying a macaroon filled them with delight, but to-day they wished and wished that there wasn't a macaroon in the world.

"*Now* where?" demanded Michael, hopping from one leg to the other in his anxiety to know if there were any of the Pound Note left. He felt sure there couldn't be and yet—he hoped.

"Home," said Mary Poppins.

Their faces fell. There was no change, after all, not even a penny or Mary Poppins would surely have spent it. But Mary Poppins, as she dumped the bag of macaroons up on Annabel's chest and strode ahead, had such a look on her face that they did not dare to make any remark. They only knew that, for once, she had disappointed them and they felt they could not forgive her.

"But—this isn't the way home," complained Michael, dragging his feet so that his toes scraped along the pavement.

"Isn't the Park on the way home, I'd like to know?" she demanded, turning fiercely upon him.

"Yes—but—"

"There are more ways than one of going through a Park," she remarked and led them round to a side of it they had never seen before.

The sun shone warmly down. The tall trees bowed over the railings and rustled their leaves. Up in the branches two sparrows were fighting over a piece of straw. A squirrel hopped along the stone balustrade and sat up on his hindquarters, asking for nuts.

But to-day these things did not matter. Jane and Michael were not interested. All they could think of was the fact that Mary Poppins had spent the whole Pound Note on unimportant things and had kept nothing over.

Tired and disappointed, they trailed after her towards the Gates.

Over the entrance, a new one they had never seen

before, spread a tall stone arch, splendidly carved with a Lion and a Unicorn. And beneath the arch sat an old, old woman, her face as grey as the stone itself and as withered and wrinkled as a walnut. On her little old knees she held a tray piled up with what looked like small coloured strips of rubber and above her head, tied firmly to the Park railings, a cluster of bright balloons bobbed and bounced and bounded.

"Balloons! Balloons!" shouted Jane. And, loosening her hand from John's sticky fingers, she ran towards the old woman. Michael bounded after her, leaving Barbara alone and lost in the middle of the pavement.

"Well, my deary ducks!" said the Balloon Woman in an old cracked voice. "Which will you have? Take your choice! And take your time!" She leant forward and shook her tray in front of them.

"We only came to look," Jane explained. "We've got no money."

"Tch, tch, tch! What's the good of *looking* at a balloon? You've got to feel a balloon, you've got to hold a balloon, you've got to *know* a balloon! Coming to look! What good will that do you?"

The old woman's voice crackled like a little flame. She rocked herself on her stool.

Jane and Michael stared at her helplessly. They knew she was speaking the truth. But what could they do?

"When I was a girl," the old woman went on, "people really *understood* balloons. They didn't just come and look! They took—yes, they *took*! There wasn't a child that went through these gates without one. They wouldn't have insulted the Balloon Woman in those days by just looking and passing by!"

She bent her head back and gazed up at the bouncing balloons above her.

"Ah, my loves and doves!" she cried. "They don't understand you any more—nobody but the old woman understands. You're old-fashioned now. Nobody wants you!"

"We *do* want one," said Michael stoutly. "But we haven't any money. *she* spent the whole Pound Note on—"

"And who is 'she'?" enquired a voice close behind him.

He turned and his face went pink.

"I meant—er—that you—er—" he began nervously.

"Speak politely of your betters!" remarked Mary Poppins and, stretching her arm over his shoulder, she put half-a-crown on the Balloon Woman's tray.

Michael stared at it, shining there among the limp un-blown balloons.

"Then there was some change over!" said Jane, wishing she had not thought so crossly of Mary Poppins.

The Balloon Woman, her old eyes sparkling, picked up the coin, and gazed at it for a long moment.

"Shiny, shiny, King-and-Crown!" she cried. "I haven't seen one of these since I was a girl." She cocked her head at Mary Poppins. "Do you want a balloon, my lass?"

"*If* you please!" said Mary Poppins with haughty politeness.

"How many, my deary-duck, how many?"

"Four!"

Jane and Michael, almost jumping out of their skins, turned and flung their arms round her.

"Oh, Mary Poppins, do you mean it? One each? Really-really?"

"I hope I always say what I mean," she said primly, looking very conceited.

They sprang towards the tray and began to turn over the coloured balloon-cases.

The Balloon Woman slipped the silver coin into a pocket in her skirt. "There, my shiny!" she said, giving the pocket a loving pat. Then, with excited trembling hands, she helped the children turn over the cases.

"Go carefully, my deary-ducks!" she warned them. "Remember, there's balloons *and* balloons, and one for everybody! Take your choice and take your time. There's many a child got the wrong balloon and his life was never the same after."

"I'll have this one!" said Michael, choosing a yellow one with red markings.

"Well, let me blow it up and you can see if it's the right one!" said the Balloon Woman.

She took it from him and with one gigantic puff blew it up. Zip! There it was! You would hardly think such a tiny person could have so much breath in her body. The yellow balloon, neatly marked with red, bobbed at the end of its string.

"But, I say!" said Michael staring. "It's got my name on it!"

And, sure enough, the red markings on the balloon were letters spelling out the two words—"MICHAEL BANKS."

"Aha!" cackled the Balloon Woman. "What did I tell you? You took your time and the choice was right!"

"See if mine is!" said Jane, handing the Balloon Woman a limp blue balloon.

She puffed and blew it up and there appeared across the fat blue globe the words "JANE CAROLINE BANKS" in large white letters.

"Is that your name, my deary-duck?" said the Balloon Woman.

Jane nodded.

The Balloon Woman laughed to herself, a thin, old cackling laugh, as Jane took the balloon from her and bounced it on the air.

"Me! Me!" cried John and Barbara, plunging fat hands among the balloon-cases. John drew out a pink one and, as she blew it up, the Balloon Woman smiled. There, round the balloon, the words could clearly be seen. "JOHN AND BARBARA BANKS—ONE BETWEEN THEM BECAUSE THEY ARE TWINS."

"But," said Jane, "I don't understand. How did you know? You never saw us before."

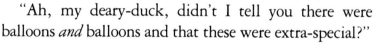

"Ah, my deary-duck, didn't I tell you there were balloons *and* balloons and that these were extra-special?"

"But did you put the names on them?" said Michael.

"I?" the old woman chuckled. "Nary I!"

"Then who did?"

"Ask me another, my deary-duck! All I know is that the names *are* there! And there's a balloon for everybody in the world if only they choose properly."

"One for Mary Poppins, too?"

The Balloon Woman, cocked her head and looked at Mary Poppins with a curious smile.

"Let her try!" She rocked herself on her little stool. "Take your choice and take your time! Choose and see!"

Mary Poppins sniffed importantly. Her hand hovered for a moment over the empty balloons and then pounced on a red one. She held it out at arm's length and, to their astonishment, the children saw it slowly filling with air of it's own accord. Larger and larger it grew till it became the size of Michael's. But still it swelled until it was three times as large as any other balloon. And across it appeared in letters of gold the two words "MARY POPPINS."

The red balloon bounced through the air and the old woman tied a string to it and with a little cackling laugh, handed it back to Mary Poppins.

Up into the dancing air danced the four balloons. They tugged at their strings as though they wanted to be free of their moorings. The wind caught them and flung them backwards and forwards, to the North, to the South, to the East, to the West.

"Balloons *and* balloons, my deary-ducks! One for everybody if only they knew it!" cried the Balloon Woman, happily.

At that moment an elderly gentleman in a top hat, turning in at the Park Gates, looked across and saw the balloons. The children saw him give a little start. Then he hurried up to the Balloon Woman.

"How much?" he said, jingling his money in his pocket.

"Sevenpence halfpenny. Take your choice and take your time!"

He took a brown one and the Balloon Woman blew it up. The words "The Honourable WILLIAM WETH-ERILL WILKINS" appeared on it in green letters.

"Good Gracious!" said the elderly gentleman. "Good gracious, that's *my* name!"

"You choose well, my deary-duck. Balloons *and* balloons!" said the old woman.

The elderly gentleman stared at his balloon as it tugged at its string.

"Extraordinary!" he said, and blew his nose with a trumpeting sound. "Forty years ago, when I was a boy, I tried to buy a balloon here. But they wouldn't let me. Said they couldn't afford it. Forty years—and it's been waiting for me all this time. Most extraordinary!"

And he hurried away, bumping into the arch because his eyes were fixed on the balloon. The children saw him giving little excited leaps in the air as he went.

"Look at him!" cried Michael as the Elderly Gentleman bobbed higher and higher. But at that moment

his own balloon began pulling at the string and he felt himself lifted off his feet.

"Hello, hello! How funny! Mine's doing it, too!"

"Balloons *and* balloons, my deary-duck!" said the Balloon Woman and broke into her cackling laugh as the Twins, both holding their balloon by its single string, bounced off the ground.

"I'm going, I'm going!" shrieked Jane as she, too, was borne upwards.

"Home, please!" said Mary Poppins.

215

Immediately, the red balloon soared up, dragging Mary Poppins after it. Up and down she bounced, with Annabel and the parcels in her arms. Through the Gates and above the path the red balloon bore Mary Poppins, her hat very straight, her hair very tidy, and her feet as trimly walking the air as they usually walked the earth. Jane and Michael and the Twins, tugged jerkily up and down by their balloons, followed her.

"Oh, oh, oh!" cried Jane as she was whirled past the branch of an elm tree, "What a *delicious* feeling!"

"I feel as if I were made of air!" said Michael, knocking into a Park seat and bouncing off it again, "What a lovely way to go home!"

"O-o-h! E-e-eh!" squeaked the Twins, tossing and bobbing together.

"Best foot forward, please, and don't dawdle!" said Mary Poppins, looking fiercely over her shoulder, for all the world as if they were walking sedately on the ground instead of being tugged through the air.

Past the Park Keeper's house they went and down the Lime Walk. The Elderly Gentleman was there bouncing along ahead of them.

Michael turned for a moment and looked behind him.

"Look, Jane, look! Everybody's got one!"

She turned. In the distance a group of people, all carrying balloons, were being jerked up and down in the air.

"The Ice Cream Man has bought one!" she cried, staring and just missing a statue.

"Yes, and the Sweep! And there—do you see?—is Miss Lark!"

Across the lawn a familiar figure came bouncing, hatted and gloved, and holding a balloon bearing the name "LUCINDA EMILY LARK." She bobbed across the Elm Walk, looking very pleased and dignified, and disappeared round the edge of a fountain.

By this time the Park was filling with people and every one of them had a balloon with a name on it and

every one was bouncing in the air.

"Heave ho, there! Room for the Admiral! Where's my port? Heave ho!" shouted a huge, nautical voice as Admiral and Mrs. Boom went rolling through the air. They held the string of a large white balloon with their name on it in blue letters.

"Masts and mizzens! Cockles and shrimps! Haul away, my hearties!" roared Admiral Boom, carefully avoiding a large oak tree.

The crowd of balloons and people grew thicker. There was hardly a patch of air in the Park that was not rain-bowy with balloons. Jane and Michael could see Mary Poppins threading her way primly among them and they, too, hurried through the throng, with John and Barbara bobbing at their heels.

"Oh, dear! Oh, dear! My balloon won't bounce me. I must have chosen the wrong one!" said a voice at Jane's elbow.

An old-fashioned lady with a quill in her hat and a feather boa round her neck was standing on the path just below Jane. At her feet lay a purple balloon across which was written in letters of gold, "THE PRIME MINISTER."

"What shall I do?" she cried. "The old woman at the Gates said, "Take your choice and take your time, my deary-duck!" and I did. But I've got the wrong one. *I'm* not the Prime Minister!"

"Excuse me, but I am!" said a voice at her side, as a tall man, very elegantly dressed and carrying a rolled umbrella, stepped up to her.

The lady turned, "Oh, then this is your balloon! Let me see if you've got mine!"

The Prime Minister, whose balloon was not bouncing him at all, showed it to her. Its name was "LADY MURIEL BRIGHTON-JONES."

"Yes, you have! We've got mixed!" she cried, and handing the Prime Minister his balloon, she seized her own. Presently they were off the ground, and flying among the trees, talking as they went.

"Are you married?" Jane and Michael heard Lady Muriel ask.

And the Prime Minister answered, "No. I can't find the right sort of middle-aged lady—not too young and not too old and rather jolly because I'm so serious myself."

"Would I do?" said Lady Muriel Brighton-Jones. "I enjoy myself quite a lot."

"Yes, I think you'd do very nicely," said the Prime Minister and, hand in hand, they joined the tossing throng.

By this time the Park was really rather crowded. Jane and Michael, bobbing across the lawns after Mary Poppins, constantly bumped into other bouncing figures who had bought balloons from the Balloon Woman. A tall man, wearing a long moustache, a blue suit and a helmet, was being tugged through the air by a balloon marked "POLICE INSPECTOR"; and another, bearing the words "LORD MAYOR," dragged along a round, fat person in a three-cornered hat, a red overall, and a large brass necklace.

"Move on, please! Don't crowd the Park. Observe the Regulations! All litter to be Deposited in the Rubbish Baskets!"

The Park Keeper, roaring and ranting, and holding

a small cherry-coloured balloon marked "F. SMITH," threaded his way through the crowd. With a wave of his hand he moved on two dogs—a bull-dog with the word "CU" written on his balloon and a fox-terrier whose name appeared to be "ALBERTINE."

"Leave my dogs alone! Or I shall take your number and report you!" cried a lady whose balloon said she was "THE DUCHESS OF MAYFIELD."

But the Park Keeper took no notice and went bobbing by, crying "All Dogs on a Lead! Don't crowd the Park! No Smoking! Observe the Regulations!" till his voice was hoarse.

"Where's Mary Poppins?" said Michael, whisking up to Jane.

"There! Just ahead of us!" she replied and pointed to the prim, tidy figure that bounced at the end of the largest balloon in the Park. They followed it homewards.

"Balloons *and* balloons, my deary-ducks!" cried a cackling voice behind them.

And, turning, they saw the Balloon Woman. Her tray was empty and there was not a balloon anywhere near her, but in spite of that she was flying through the air as though a hundred invisible balloons were drawing her onwards.

"Every one sold!" she screamed as she sped by. "There's a balloon for every one if only they knew it. They took their choice and they took their time! And I've sold the lot! Balloons *and* balloons."

Her pockets jingled richly as she flew by and, standing still in the air, Jane and Michael watched the small, withered figure shooting past the bobbing balloons, past the Prime Minister and the Lord Mayor, past Mary Poppins and Annabel, until the tiny shape grew tinier still and the Balloon Woman disappeared into the distance.

"Balloons and balloons, my deary-ducks!" The faint echo came drifting back to them.

"Step along, please!" said Mary Poppins. They flocked

round her, all four of them. Annabel, rocked by the movement of Mary Poppins' balloon, nestled closer to her and went to sleep.

The gate of Number Seventeen stood open, the front door was ajar. Mary Poppins, leaping neatly and bouncing primly, passed through and up the stairs. The children followed, jumping and bobbing. And when they reached the Nursery door, their four pairs of feet clattered noisily to the ground. Mary Poppins floated down and landed without a sound.

"Oh, what a *lovely* afternoon!" said Jane, rushing to fling her arms round Mary Poppins.

"Well, that's more than *you* are, at this moment. Brush your hair, please. I don't care for scarecrows," Mary Poppins said tartly.

"I feel like a balloon myself," said Michael joyfully, "All airy-fairy-free!"

"I'd be sorry for the fairy that looked like you!" said Mary Poppins. "Go and wash your hands. You're no better than a sweep!"

221

When they came back, clean and tidy, the four balloons were resting against the ceiling, their strings firmly moored behind the picture over the mantelpiece.

Michael gazed up at them—his own yellow one, Jane's blue, the Twins' pink, and Mary Poppins' red. They were very still. No breath of wind moved them. Light and bright, steady and still, they leaned against the ceiling.

"I wonder!" said Michael softly, half to himself.

"You wonder what?" said Mary Poppins, sorting out her parcels.

"I wonder if it would all have happened if you hadn't been with us."

Mary Poppins sniffed.

"I shouldn't wonder if you didn't wonder much too much!" she replied.

And with that Michael had to be content.

Many years ago the village blacksmith was one of the most important people in town. At his forge the blacksmith produced all the ironwork needed by his townsmen, including horseshoes, hinges, wheel rims, and farm implements. This poem by Henry Wadsworth Longfellow was first published in 1840, but the steady, hard-working smith is still a model for us all.

The Village Blacksmith

Henry Wadsworth Longfellow

UNDER a spreading chestnut tree
  The village smithy stands;
The smith, a mighty man is he,
  With large and sinewy hands;
And the muscles of his brawny arms
  Are strong as iron bands.

His hair is crisp, and black, and long,
  His face is like the tan;
His brow is wet with honest sweat,
  He earns whate'er he can,
And looks the whole world in the face,
  For he owes not any man.

Week in, week out, from morn till night,
  You can hear his bellows blow;
You can hear him swing his heavy sledge,
  With measured beat and slow,
Like a sexton ringing the village bell,
  When the evening sun is low.

And children coming home from school
    Look in at the open door;
They love to see the flaming forge,
    And hear the bellows roar,
And catch the burning sparks that fly
    Like chaff from a threshing floor.

He goes on Sunday to the church,
    And sits among his boys;
He hears the parson pray and preach,
    He hears his daughter's voice,
Singing in the village choir,
    And it makes his heart rejoice.

It sounds to him like her mother's voice,
    Singing in Paradise!
He needs must think of her once more,
    How in the grave she lies;
And with his hard, rough hand he wipes
    A tear out of his eyes.

Toiling,—rejoicing,—sorrowing,
    Onward through life he goes;
Each morning sees some task begin,
    Each evening sees it close;
Something attempted, something done,
    Has earned a night's repose.

Thanks, thanks to thee, my worthy friend,
    For the lesson thou hast taught!
Thus at the flaming forge of life
    Our fortunes must be wrought;
Thus on its sounding anvil shaped
    Each burning deed and thought.